Now I Know! 3

Workbook

Catherine Zgouras

Contents

1	How do we find our way?	Page 4
2	How do we know about the past?	Page 18
3	Why do we go on vacation?	Page 32
4	Why do we tell stories?	Page 46
5	Why take care of the environment?	Page 60
6	Why do we use numbers every day?	Page 74
7	What do we do for entertainment?	Page 88
8	Why is space interesting?	Page 102
9	How are homes different?	Page 116
10	How do we take care of our body?	Page 130
11	Why is Antarctica special?	Page 144
12	Why do we have festivals?	Page 158

1 How do we find our way?

1 What do you know about maps? Write two ways maps can help you.

....

....

2 Circle the places in your town. Then think about and write one thing you learn in this unit.

    mountain   bank   bus station   hospital
    desert   park   restaurant   shopping mall

....

3 ▶ 1-1 BBC Watch the video. Then number the places on the map.

1 road   5 cinema
2 river   6 information centre
3 library   7 restaurant
4 bank

4 ▶ 1-1 BBC Read and match. Watch the video again and check.

1 We use a map to
2 The buildings on a map
3 To read a map correctly, you need to
4 Every building or place on a map
5 To cross the river, you need to

a   are to scale. This means they're small.
b   has its own symbol.
c   find where we want to go.
d   go over the bridge.
e   hold it the right way up.

4

Vocabulary 1

1 Look and circle.

building
square

square
downtown

below
above

map
sign

above
below

close to
beside

2 Read and match.

1 a drawing that shows you where places are   a cross
2 you do this to get from one side of the street to the other   b close to
3 a big structure that has walls and a roof   c map
4 not far away from   d building

3 Complete the sentences. Use the words from Activities 1 and 2.

1 My school is very _____ my house, so I walk to school.
2 When the light is green, it's safe to _____ the street.
3 I live on the third floor. My friend lives _____ me on the fourth floor.
4 The movie theater is _____ the restaurant. Go down the stairs.

4 Look at the picture and write four sentences about it.

above   below   building   cross   downtown   sign

Vocabulary challenge: parts of a city

5 Look, read, and match.

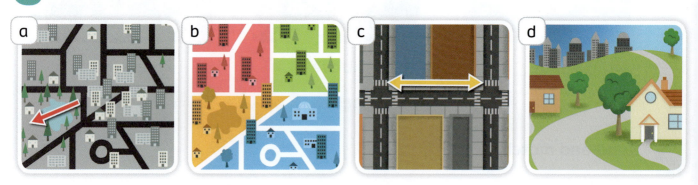

1 **Block** is the distance from one street to another.
2 The **outskirts** of a city are far away from downtown.
3 **Suburbs** is an area where people live outside a city.
4 A city is divided into a number of **precincts**.

6 Read and write.

1 There's a new police station in our _____ .
2 My parents were tired of living in the city so they moved to the _____ .
3 Tom lives only a few _____ away from his school.
4 My family and I live on the _____ of Chicago. It takes us a long time to get downtown.

6

Reading 1

1 Look at the picture. Why are the mice climbing into the bag? Then read the story. Were your predictions correct?

Pedro and George Save the Day

A mysterious woman is stealing the Queen's diaries and secret letters from the Royal Museum Library. Two mice, George and Pedro, want to stop her. They find her at a train station downtown.

The woman is reading a magazine. She's waiting for her train. George stops beside the woman's bag. He looks at Pedro. "Wait here," he says. Then he quietly opens the bag. He climbs inside and quickly grabs the diaries and letters. He gives them to Pedro. But then they hear a loud "Bong! Bong! Bong!"

The woman looks at her watch, and at a sign on the wall opposite her. Then she reaches down to put her magazine in her bag.

"Hey! What's going on?" she says. "Help! Thieves!" she shouts.

"Quick, Pedro," says George. "Run!" The mice start running fast and the woman runs behind them.

A big man with two large bags is walking into the train station. The mice quickly run between his legs. Then Pedro hears the woman shout! He looks back. She's on the floor, and the big man is talking to her and trying to help her get up.

"Sorry," he says. "Are you OK?"

"No!" she says. "Get out of my way! Where are they?"

She looks around, but she can't see Pedro and George. They got away! They're on their way to the Royal Museum Library to return the diaries and letters.

2 Read and match.

1 Who are the main characters?
2 Where does the action take place?
3 What do the mice want to get back?
4 Why do the mice go to the library?

a a train station
b to return the letters and diaries
c Pedro, George, and the woman
d the Queen's diaries and letters

3 What should you do if you see someone stealing?

7

Grammar 1

✓	✗
Cross the street here.	**Don't cross** the street here.
Please **say** your name.	Please **don't say** your name.
Turn left at the square.	**Don't turn** left at the square.

1 The sentences above are instructions.
2 People say *please* when they want to be polite.

1 Look, read, and match.

Please be quiet. ☐   Don't eat in class. ☐
Don't play games in class. ☐   Please close the door. ☐

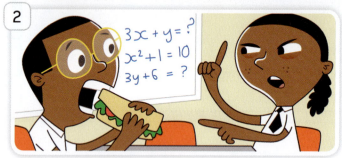

2 Complete the sentences. Use the positive (✓) or negative (✗) form.

1 Please _____ (✓ open) the door.
2 _____ (✗ be) noisy.
3 _____ (✗ close) the window, please.
4 Let's _____ (✓ help) the teacher.
5 Please _____ (✗ run).
6 _____ (✓ make) your bed, please.

3 Look and read. Then choose and write.

feed   run   sit   talk   turn   walk

1. .... in the library.
2. .... the animals at the zoo.
3. .... beside the harbor.
4. .... on that chair, please.
5. .... on the grass.
6. .... left at the museum.

4 What rules do you have in your class? Write.

1 ....
2 ....
3 ....

Vocabulary 2

1 Write the letters in order.

1 l g a o n ....
2 p u ....
3 o n d u r a ....
4 w o d n ....

2 Look and read. Choose and write.

recreation center

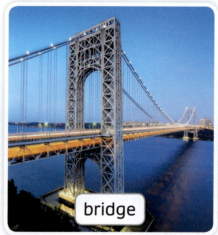
bridge

harbor

museum

theater

art gallery

1 This is an area of calm water where ships are safe. ....
2 This is a place where you can see old things. ....
3 You can walk on this to cross a river. ....
4 People go there to see paintings. ....
5 This is a place where you can watch a play. ....
6 You can go here to play basketball. ....

10

3 **Mark where you want the museum, theater, and recreation center to be. Then write how to get there from the harbor.**

1 museum   2 theater   3 recreation center

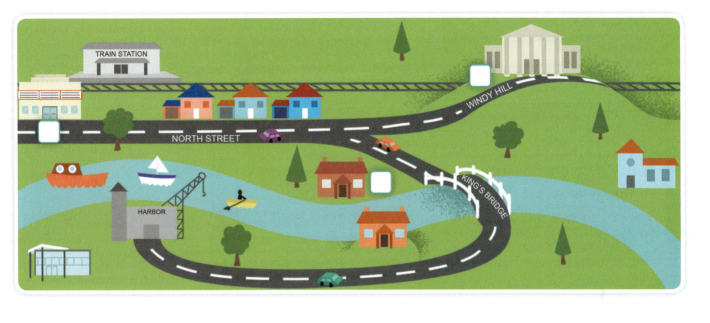

....
....
....

Word study: compound words

4 **Match and write.**

1 shopping — station
2 art — mall
3 train — pool
4 recreation — center
5 swimming — gallery

shopping mall
....
....
....
....

5 **Read and complete. Use the words from Activity 4.**

A new ¹ .... opened in our town. It has some really cool stores! It's close to the ² ...., so it's easy to get to from other towns. The mall even has an ³ .... with some fantastic paintings. There's also a ⁴ .... where I play different sports. The only thing missing is a ⁵ ....

11

Reading 2

1 Read Amy's blog and write the headings.

~~Friday: the Dubai Mall~~   Saturday afternoon: Dubai Museum
Thursday morning: Dubai by boat   Saturday morning: the Burj Khalifa

a ....

Today we were up early because we wanted to do lots of things. The first thing was a boat trip round Dubai. The cruise was one and a half hours. We looked at all the skyscrapers and beautiful buildings. There aren't any skyscrapers in my city. The ones in Dubai were amazing.

b *Friday: the Dubai Mall* ....

I spent the Friday of my holiday at the Dubai Mall. It was fantastic. There isn't anywhere like this at home! It has more than 1,200 shops, an ice rink, an aquarium and some very big fountains.

c ....

160 storeys! That's how tall the Burj Khalifa is. There was a very fast lift to take us up to the 125th floor. We were 456 metres high in the air! I was afraid, but it was amazing. There's a café where you can drink coffee and look at the views.

d ....

Here we learnt about the history of old Dubai. The museum is in an old fort. Inside there are some old boats, traditional houses and furniture. It was very interesting to learn about old Dubai because the rest of the city is very modern.

2 Read and circle **T** (true) or **F** (false).

1 Amy's city doesn't have skyscrapers.   T   F
2 Amy was afraid of the coffee in the Burj Khalifa.   T   F
3 The museum is in a new building.   T   F

3 Is it important to find out about a place before you go there? Why?/Why not?

Grammar 2

Where **does** the Doctor **live**?
He **lives** in the blue box.

Does he **often come** to London?
Yes, he **does**.

He **doesn't visit** London **every day**.

He and Kim **sometimes travel** in space and time.

What **are** you **doing** here?
I**'m walking** around the city.

Are you **looking** for aliens **today**?
Yes, I **am**.

Kim **isn't running at the moment**.
She**'s walking**.

1 Read and write *R* (routines) or *N* (happening now).

1 They often go to the park. ....
2 Are they swimming right now? ....
3 She isn't having lunch at home today. ....
4 Does he walk to school? ....
5 I'm reading my favorite book this afternoon. ....
6 We don't ride our bikes every day. ....

2 Read and circle.

1 Joe is talking about his new skateboard **now** / **every day**.
2 Does she study in the library **now** / **on Tuesdays**?
3 Is your mom helping you with your homework **today** / **sometimes**?
4 Do you **right now** / **often** look for information on the internet?
5 Jack doesn't listen to music **every day** / **today**.

3 Complete the sentences for you.

1 I .... (ride) a bike now.
2 I .... (go) to school every day.
3 I .... (write) in my book at the moment.
4 I .... (call) grandma once a week.

13

4 It's Monday evening. Look and write what the children usually do and what they are doing now.

	Usually	Now
1 Mona		
2 Steve		
3 Rina		

1 Mona usually plays tennis on Monday evenings. She isn't playing tennis now. She's studying for a test.

2 ....

3 ....

5 Write the questions in order. Then answer for you.

1 you / day / homework / every / do / have

.... ?

....

2 now / Italian / speaking / you / are

.... ?

....

3 afternoon / the / what / usually / do / do / you / in

.... ?

....

14

Writing

1 Which words mean *very good*? Read and circle.

awesome   fine   great   OK

amazing   fantastic   good   nice

2 Look at your pictures of a recreation center. Write two sentences about it using different words for *very good*.

1 ....
2 ....

3 Read and make notes about the recreation center.

1 What's the name of the place?
....

2 When is it open?
....

3 What can you do there?
Indoors: ....
Outdoors: ....

4 How do you get there?
....

4 Write about the recreation center. Use your ideas from Activities 2 and 3 to help you.

(!) Remember
1 Write a title.
2 Use paragraphs.
3 Use different words for *very good*.
4 Check spelling.

Now I Know

1 Read and circle.

1 The recreation center is **along** / **beside** / **close** to the swimming pool.
2 If I get lost, I can look at a **sign** / **building** / **street** to find my way.
3 I enjoy shopping **down** / **downtown** / **at the museum**.
4 You can **cross** / **beside** / **above** the street. The light is green.

2 Read and write the words in bold next to the correct sentence.

1 There are many tall **maps** downtown. ....
2 We learned about history at the **harbor**. ....
3 Look at the **theater**! It's so long! ....
4 **Buildings** help you find your way around town. ....
5 The **bridge** has a fantastic play tonight. ....
6 We saw many beautiful ships at the **museum**. ....

3 Look, choose, and complete the instructions.

feed   put   ride   run   sit   turn

1 .... bikes.
2 .... your trash in the trash can.
3 Please .... the animals.
4 .... on the steps, please.
5 .... in the hall.
6 .... left.

4 Read and complete.

1. We .... (usually/play) basketball in the afternoon.
2. .... (your dad/work) today?
3. Sami .... (not ride) his bike downtown this morning.
4. .... (Amal/often/help) her sister?

5 Look and write.

1. every morning — now
2. every Friday — now
3. every Monday — now

1 *He runs every morning, but now he's watching TV.*
2 ....
3 ....

Things I learn

1. **What are your three favorite words in this unit?**

....

2. **Write something you think is interesting about:**

maps ....
places in a city ....

3. **Which places do you often go to? How do you find your way?**

....
....

17

2 How do we know about the past?

1 What do you know about the past? Where did you learn them?

....

....

2 Circle the things that you could see a long time ago. Then think about and write one thing you learn in this unit.

    castle   dinosaur   hospital   knight

    movie star   pyramid   shopping mall

....

3 BBC 2-1 Watch the video. Then look and match.

tyrannosaurus rex ☐   stegosaurus ☐

diplodocus ☐   triceratops ☐

a   b   c   d

4 BBC 2-1 Read the sentences and circle T (true) or F (false). Watch the video again and check.

1 We can't see dinosaurs today because they're hiding. T F
2 The dinosaurs died 230 million years ago. T F
3 The stegosaurus ate plants and fruit. T F
4 The tyrannosaurus rex ate plants. T F
5 The triceratops didn't eat meat. T F
6 The diplodocus had a really long neck. T F

Vocabulary 1

1 Read and match.

1. herbivore
2. carnivore
3. horn
4. extinct
5. quick
6. loud

a. describes something that no longer exists
b. an animal that only eats plants
c. a hard, pointed body part on top of an animal's head
d. describes something that makes a lot of noise
e. an animal that eats other animals
f. describes something that moves fast

2 Read and circle.

What do you know about crocodiles?

Crocodiles are ¹ **dinosaurs / carnivores**. They eat fish, birds, and other animals. They have long ² **horns / tails** that help them swim. Crocodiles are very ³ **loud / quick** in the water and on land – they can swim and run at 15 km per hour. They can also make ⁴ **loud / quick** sounds. Did you know crocodiles were alive at the same time as ⁵ **dinosaurs / herbivores**? Dinosaurs are now ⁶ **careful / extinct**, but crocodiles aren't! We need to protect them and make sure they aren't all ⁷ **quick / dead** in the next few years.

3 Read and complete. Use the words you didn't circle in Activity 2.

WHAT DO YOU KNOW ABOUT THE PENTACERATOPS?

The triceratops is a very famous ¹ _____, but do you know about the pentaceratops? The name "pentaceratops" means "five ² _____". But, in fact, they only had three, like a triceratops. The two on the side of their faces were just bones. Also like a triceratops, they didn't eat meat – so they were ³ _____. They were about seven meters long but they still had to be ⁴ _____ of big carnivores.

4 Write about each animal. Use the words from Activity 1.

1 Cows *are herbivores. They have* ....
2 Elephants ....
3 Tigers ....

Vocabulary challenge: animal categories

5 Read, look, and match.

Kinds of animals

1 Mammals ☐
- have hair or fur
- their babies drink milk

2 Reptiles ☐
- have short legs and long tails
- lay eggs
- their body temperature changes

3 Birds ☐
- can fly
- lay eggs

4 Amphibians ☐
- lay eggs
- can live in water and on land
- their body temperature changes

5 Fish ☐
- live in water
- lay eggs

a b c d e

6 Complete the sentences.

1 .... don't lay eggs.
2 .... can't live on land.
3 The body temperature of .... and .... goes down when it's cold.
4 .... fly high in the sky.

20

Reading 1

1 Read *A World Long Ago*. Does the story happen in more than one place?

A WORLD LONG AGO

Barl and Lom are fishing. Two little mammoths come to the river. "Look!" says Barl. "They want to be friends with us."
"We can't be friends with mammoths," says Lom. "They're usually our dinner, not our friends!"
"Mammoths are herbivores," says Barl. "We eat them, but they eat plants."
"Yes, but, they're very big and they might chase us. Let's go home," says Lom.

Barl and Lom are in bed in their tent. They have a small fire to keep them warm.
"Where's Dad?" asks Barl. "It's late and it's getting dark."
"He's looking for food today," says their mother. Suddenly, they hear a loud noise.
"Help!" cries Lom. "The mammoths are here."
Slowly and carefully, they get up and look outside. They see a few men carrying lots of meat. Barl sees his father and runs to him. "Dad! You're here!"
"Yes, I am. And look at all the food we've got!"
"Did you see the mammoths? We were very scared," says Lom.
"Don't worry," says their father. "You're safe. The mammoths can't hurt you."
"But are the mammoths safe, Dad?" asks Barl. His father doesn't answer.

2 Read and match.

1 Why is Lom scared of the mammoths?
2 Why don't the mammoths eat humans?
3 Where is the children's father?
4 What food did the children's father bring?

a meat
b they're very big
c looking for food
d they're herbivores

3 Imagine you see a mammoth. How do you feel? Why?

Grammar 1

Be **quiet**.   Open the door **quietly**.
You're too **loud**.   You're speaking too **loudly**.
Kim is too **slow**.   Kim is walking too **slowly**.
Be **careful**.   Walk **carefully**.
We need to be **quick**.   We need to go **quickly**.
The dinosaur is **fast**.   The dinosaur can run **fast**.

1 Read and circle.

Dear Tyler,
Remember to listen to your teacher [1] **careful / carefully** and don't talk [2] **loud / loudly** to your friends in class. Be good at school and be [3] **nice / nicely** to your classmates. When you come home, ride your bike [4] **slow / slowly** and be careful of the cars that drive fast. Don't do your homework too quickly, and make sure your handwriting is [5] **neat / neatly**. Remember to play [6] **quiet / quietly** with your sister and don't listen to loud music. Listen to your grandma, too!
Have a great day! ☺
Mom

2 Look, read, and write. Then write one sentence about the picture.

1 The music is playing
....

2 The children are crossing the road
....

3 Where are they?
....

4 What is the woman doing?
....

5 ....

22

3 Read and complete. Then match.

carefully   quickly   quiet   slow

1 Please be .... The baby is sleeping.
2 Let's walk .... so we aren't late.
3 We must do our homework .... so we don't make mistakes.
4 Jackie runs fast, but I'm a .... runner.

a
b
c
d

4 Write the words in order. Use the correct form.

1 fast / going / you're / too
....

2 drives / dad / my / slow
....

3 is / quiet / at / Melanie / school
....

4 museum / loud / talk / don't / please / the / in
....

5 quiet / careful / work / and / we
....

5 Write five sentences to describe your friends and family.

careful   carefully   fast
loud   loudly   slow   slowly

23

Vocabulary 2

1 Listen and color.

2 Look at the picture from Activity 1. Then read, choose, and write.

> archeologists   buried   dig   exhibit   gold
> pharaohs   steps   thieves   tomb   treasure

The picture shows four ¹ .... working in Egypt. About 3,000 years ago, ² .... ruled in Egypt. The Egyptians ³ .... dead pharaohs in underground rooms.

When the archeologists walk down the ⁴ .... into the room, they see a large ⁵ .... in the middle. There's also a box full of beautiful ⁶ ...., like silver and ⁷ .... jewelry. There's a lot of dirt on the ground. The archeologists need to ⁸ .... to find out what's under the dirt. There are two more people in the picture. Who are they? Oh, no! They're ⁹ .... They want to sell the treasure so it can't be an ¹⁰ .... in a museum.

3 Imagine you work at a museum. What things do you put in an exhibit?

Word study: different kinds of words

4 Complete the chart. Then add your own words.

careful   dig   dinosaur   loud   quietly
slowly   treasure   walk

Actions	Names of people or things	Words to describe people or things	Words to describe actions
bury	pharaoh	tall	quickly

5 Look at the chart from Activity 4. Read and circle the words in the correct color.

1. Thieves dig quickly to find the treasure.
2. Archeologists work carefully.
3. People talk quietly in the big museum.
4. You walk slowly when you're tired.
5. My dad is a careful driver.

Reading 2

1 Read the magazine article. Choose the correct first sentence for each paragraph

a For more than 1,700 years, the buildings were under the ground.

c Everything changed suddenly one day about 1,950 years ago.

b Now, more than two million people visit Pompeii every year.

d 2,000 years ago, Pompeii was a busy city.

Pompeii, in the past and today

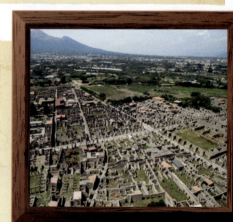

1 ☐ About 20,000 people lived there. Many people were farmers. The land close to Pompeii was very good for growing things because of ash from the volcano, Mount Vesuvius. In the summer, many rich Romans went to Pompeii. There were big houses, beautiful theaters, and other buildings.

2 ☐ Ash and rocks started to come out of Mount Vesuvius and go up into the sky. Soon, the ash and rocks started falling to the ground. It was difficult to breathe and see. The ash and rocks buried the city of Pompeii and killed many people.

3 ☐ Then, in the 18th century, some explorers discovered the city under six meters of rock and ash. Archeologists started digging and were amazed to find the city was almost the same as in A.D. 79. There were even jars of fruit and loaves of bread! Archeologists are still working in Pompeii today.

4 ☐ When you visit Pompeii, it's like going back in time. You can see the bodies of the people who died, as well as buildings, furniture, pots, food, and some graffiti. You can also walk down the streets and go inside houses, shops, and cafés.

2 Read the article again. Circle **T** (true) or **F** (false).

1 Pompeii was a good place to be a farmer. T F
2 People from Rome lived in Pompeii in the winter. T F
3 Archeologists stopped working in Pompeii in the 18th century. T F
4 You can see many things from A.D. 79 when you visit Pompeii. T F

3 💡 Why is it important for scientists to study volcanoes?

....

26

Grammar 2

You **have to** listen carefully.

Do I **have to** walk slowly? No, you **don't**.

The Doctor **has to** push the buttons carefully.

Does Kim **have to** help? No, she **doesn't**. The Doctor can do it.

You **don't have to** talk quietly.

1 Read and circle.

HOW TO BE AN ARCHEOLOGIST

1 First, you **has to / have to** go to a place with an interesting past.
2 Then you **don't have to / have to** dig in the ground.
3 You **have to / don't have to** use modern technology, but it can help you.
4 Can you see something interesting in the ground? Then you **have to / don't have to** clean it carefully with a brush.
5 When you can see all of it, you **don't have to / have to** take a lot of pictures.
6 Can you move it? You **have to / has to** be very careful so you don't break it.
7 You **have to / don't have to** give it to a museum, but maybe you should so other people can see it.

2 Read and complete. Use the words from the box.

| doesn't have to | don't have to | don't have to | has to | have to |

1 We _____ listen carefully to our teachers.
2 My brother _____ walk me to school every day. It's very far away.
3 I _____ go to school on Sunday. We finish school on Friday at 1 p.m.
4 My parents _____ help me with my homework. I can do it myself.
5 My baby sister is only three. She _____ go to school.

27

3 Read and check (✔) or cross (✘).

Hi, I'm Tina! I work at the museum. I have to work on the weekend, but I don't have to work at night. I have to explain the exhibits to the visitors. I also have to study the old things inside the museum.

Hello, my name's Tracey. I'm an archeologist. I have to study old things, too, but I have to work outside, even when it's cold and rainy! I don't have to work on the weekend or at night. And I don't have to explain things to visitors either, because there aren't any!

	work on the weekend	work at night	explain things to visitors	study old things	work outside
Tina	✔	✘			
Tracey					

4 Complete the questions. Then look at Activity 3 and write the answers.

1 .... Tina .... work outside? ....
2 .... Tina and Tracey .... study old things? ....
3 .... Tina .... work on the weekend? ....
4 .... Tracey .... talk to visitors? ....
5 .... Tina and Tracey .... work at night? ....

5 Look and write one thing each person has to do and one thing he/she doesn't have to do.

28

Writing

1 Read and underline the useful words and phrases.

The Amur leopard is almost extinct. There are only about 60 of them in the wild and they live mainly in Russia and China.

Amur leopards have long legs and thick fur that helps them survive in cold weather. They can run very fast and jump up to three meters! They live 10–15 years in the wild.

2 Make notes about an animal you like.

1 What animal is it?

2 What does it look like?

3 Is it extinct or alive?

4 Where does it live?

5 What does it eat?

6 What can/can't it do?

3 Write about your animal. Use your ideas from Activity 2 to help you.

(!) Remember
1 Write a title.
2 Use paragraphs.
3 Use interesting words and phrases.
4 Check spelling.

29

Now I Know

1 Complete the crossword.

Across

2 the opposite of quiet
4 an animal or plant that no longer exists
7 Tutankhamun was this
8 pirates steal or look for this in stories
9 where the Egyptians buried Pharaohs
10 people who steal

Down

1 a person who digs in the ground to find things from the past
3 an animal that doesn't eat meat
5 an animal that eats meat
6 you go up or down these

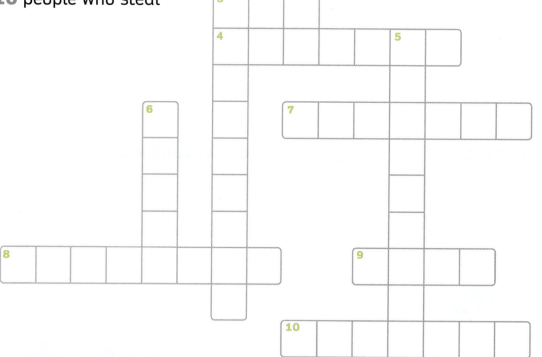

2 Read and circle.

1 The dog bites, so be **loud / careful**.
2 You can see **dinosaur / archeologist** bones in the museum.
3 A lion doesn't have a **horn / tail**, but it has a **horn / tail**.
4 The thieves **bury / dig** gold in the ground.
5 You can see **a tomb / an exhibit** of the Queen's jewels in London.

3 Look, read, and write.

Please talk ....

They're playing ....

He drives ....

4 Write the words in order. Then check (✓) the true sentences.

1   homework / carefully / do / you / to / have / your

    .... ☐

2   work / to / children / go / don't / to / have

    .... ☐

3   night / a / has / teacher / work / to / at

    .... ☐

Things I learn

1 What are your three favorite words in this unit?

....

2 Write something you think is interesting about:

dinosaurs ....

archeologists ....

3 Write two ways we can learn about the past.

....

....

31

3 Why do we go on vacation?

1 What do you know about vacations? Write two things you can do on vacation.

....

....

2 Circle the things to do with vacations. Then think about and write one thing you learn in this unit.

    beach   camping   homework   mountains   playing
    relaxing   sandcastle   studying   working

....

3 Watch the video. Then read, look, and match.

1 sheep   

2 dragon   

3 seahorse   

4 Read and circle. Watch the video again to check.

1 The teams have **all day / three hours** to build their sandcastle.
2 The design has to be **10 metres wide and 10 metres long / 10 metres tall**.
3 There are **six or seven / only seven** people in a team.
4 The design is **anything they like / always a dragon**.
5 They put water on the sandcastle because **it's fun / it gets dry**.

32

Vocabulary 1

1 Find and circle six words. Then complete the phrases.

gnh**camping**bdfgb**tent**fkrc**get**bg**clean**hh**make**wd**bag**

1 .... up
2 sleeping ....
3 .... stove
4 set up a ....
5 .... a fire
6 .... lost

2 Read and circle.

1 We must **set up a tent** / **get lost** at the campsite so we have somewhere to sleep.
2 I'm a little cold. Can you give me a **compass** / **blanket**?
3 Let's use the **flashlight** / **camping stove** to cook our fish.
4 We should always **get lost** / **clean up** after we eat, so we don't get mice and insects.
5 Don't forget your **flashlight** / **compass** so you can see in the dark.
6 Use a map and a **blanket** / **compass** to find the **campsite** / **sleeping bag**.

3 Label the things in the picture.

1 ....
2 ....
3 ....
4 ....
5 ....
6 ....

33

4 Imagine you're at a campsite. Write four things you have to do before it gets dark.

Vocabulary challenge: camping equipment

5 Read, look, and write the correct letter.

a b c d e

hiking boots | rope | matches | water bottle | insect repellent

1 We walk in them. They protect our feet.
2 We use them to make a fire.
3 A spray or cream that stops insects.
4 We drink from this.
5 We use this to tie things.

6 Read and complete. Use the words from Activity 5.

1 Make sure you put on _____ to keep the mosquitoes away.
2 We didn't make a fire because we didn't have any _____ .
3 I always have a _____ with me in case I get thirsty.
4 We used some _____ to stop the tent from falling down.
5 It's important to wear good _____ , so you don't hurt your feet.

Reading 1

1 Read the story. Number the paragraphs in order.

beginning ☐   middle ☐   end ☐

A Day at the Beach

1 When we got to the beach, we decided to have our picnic. We ate our sandwiches and we played in the sand. My sister and I made a big sandcastle. Then we dug a hole and covered Grandpa with sand. We put a big sun hat on his head. We also put a lot of sunscreen on him. It was hot so we went swimming.

2 Suddenly, we heard a man calling for help. It was Grandpa! We ran over to him and quickly dug him out of the sand. When he stood up and took off his hat, we all started laughing! The bottom half of his face was brown and the top half was white! He looked funny. We stayed at the beach all day and went home at sunset. It was a great day.

3 Yesterday was the first day of vacation. I woke up and packed my bag for a day at the beach. Then my sister and I prepared sandwiches. At nine o'clock, we got in the car and drove to the beach. Grandpa came, too.

2 Read and complete.

1. The family went to .... on the first day of vacation.
2. The girls prepared ....
3. After the picnic, the girls built a ....
4. The girls put a .... on Grandpa's head.
5. The girls forgot about grandpa because they went ....

3 What do you do on vacation to be safe and healthy?

....
....

35

Grammar 1

> The children **explored**. Dad **wanted** a relaxing vacation.
>
> I **made** a fire. We **went** to the beach last vacation. The children **slept** all the way home.
>
> The map **didn't help**. They **didn't know** the way.
>
> 1 Verbs in the past end in *-ed*.
> 2 Some verbs in the past don't end in *-ed*.
> 3 To say what you did not do in the past use **didn't** + verb

1 Read and circle.

1 Jack didn't **swim / swam** in the ocean because there were sharks.
2 We **watched / watch** the new Star Wars movie yesterday.
3 The children didn't **slept / sleep** all night because they **was / were** afraid of the dark.
4 We **makes / made** a fire at the campsite.
5 We didn't **took / take** the compass with us and we **got / get** lost.

2 Read and complete. Use the correct form of the words in the box.

> eat   go   have   make   visit

Last week, we ¹ _____ my grandparents. Grandma had cookies, cake, and milk ready for us when we got there. Before lunch, we ² _____ to the swimming pool because it was a very hot day. In the evening, we ³ _____ pizza and Grandpa told us about his school days as we ⁴ _____ . It was a great day and we ⁵ _____ a lot of fun.

3 Did you do these things yesterday? Write positive or negative sentences.

1 make breakfast

2 go to the beach

3 help my dad clean up

4 sing songs around the campfire

5 have pasta for dinner

4 Find, circle, and write the words in the past. Then use them to write true sentences about you.

D	S	S	W	A	M	I	A
I	A	Y	G	S	A	N	G
D	W	T	H	I	K	G	E
R	T	M	A	D	E	E	E
T	O	O	K	R	L	M	B

swim — *swam*
sing
make
do
see
take

1 I swam in the ocean last summer.
2
3
4
5
6

37

Vocabulary 2

1 Look, choose, and write.

> go kayaking   go rock climbing   go zip lining   meet new people

2 Read and complete. Use the words from the box.

> beautiful   coast   heavy   light   unsafe   waterfall

1 Rock climbing can be _____ if you aren't careful.
2 Your bag is as _____ as a feather. Is there anything in it?
3 Be careful with the boxes. They're very _____ .
4 I got a _____ new pair of shoes yesterday.
5 We live close to the _____ and go swimming in the ocean every day.
6 There's a very high _____ at the park.

38

3 Look, read, and write. Then write one sentence about the picture.

1   The man's backpack is very ....
2   The girl isn't swimming because it's ....
3   What is the woman holding? ....
4   What are the boys doing? ....
5   ....

Word study: *go, play, do*

4 Match and write.

go
play
do

cricket
ballet
tennis
rock climbing
kayaking
yoga

play cricket
....
....
....
....
....

5 Read and complete. Use the words from Activity 4.

1   You have to be very flexible to do .... or ....
2   You can play .... and .... at the recreation center.
3   Let's go .... or .... this weekend.

39

Reading 2

1 Read Lisa's review. Write in which paragraph you can find the information.

a Why Lisa enjoyed the camp.   paragraph ☐
b How long the course lasted.   paragraph ☐
c What Lisa did on the first day.   paragraph ☐
d Who the instructors were and what they were like.   paragraph ☐

The RADICAL ROCK Climbing Centre

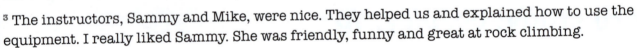

¹ This school was amazing. I took a four-week course. I didn't know how to climb before, but I do now! I wanted to learn to climb to be ready for my summer rock climbing camp. I went in the afternoons after school and on Saturday mornings. They gave us special shoes and a helmet because it's important to be safe.

² I went to the summer camp they organised, too. On the first day we went hiking. We walked to a beautiful waterfall. We were very hot so we went swimming. After that, we went climbing for the first time. It was a little difficult and sometimes scary, but it was incredible!

³ The instructors, Sammy and Mike, were nice. They helped us and explained how to use the equipment. I really liked Sammy. She was friendly, funny and great at rock climbing.

⁴ I enjoyed the camp because I met lots of new people. I also enjoyed doing the activities and being outside. I learnt that I can do anything if I try, even things I find scary. I hope I can go to the camp again next summer!
Lisa, aged 10

2 Read and match.

1 Lisa went hiking   a trying new activities.
2 They walked   b for keeping the children safe.
3 Sammy and Mike were responsible   c on the first day of summer camp.
4 Lisa enjoyed   d to a beautiful waterfall.

3 💡 Why is it important to try new activities?

Grammar 2

Did Marta **go** to summer camp?	Yes, she **did**.
Did you **like** the tutors?	No, I **didn't**.
Did they learn to **make** scenery?	Yes, they **did**.
What did you **do** at camp?	I **made** a video game.
Where did she **go**?	She **went** to the coast.
Why did Paul **go** to sports camp?	He **went** there because he likes sports.
Who did they **meet**?	They **met** new people.
How did you **get** there?	We **went** by car.
When did Mario **make** a computer game?	He **made** a computer game last month.

1 Read and circle.

1 **Did he go** / **Did he went** to the bookstore last week?
2 **Did you played** / **Did you play** video games with Matt yesterday?
3 **Did you see** / **Did see** your friends the day before yesterday?
4 Did Jean **swim** / **swam** in the ocean last summer?

2 Read and complete. Use the words in parentheses.

1 Who *did you visit* _____ (you/visit)?
   We _____ Mom's friend.
2 What _____ (John/make)?
   He _____ a fire.
3 When _____ (she/go) to Italy?
   She _____ there last summer.

We can use time phrases to talk about the past.

yesterday   the day before yesterday
last week   last summer/month/year/night

41

3 Write questions. Then look and write answers.

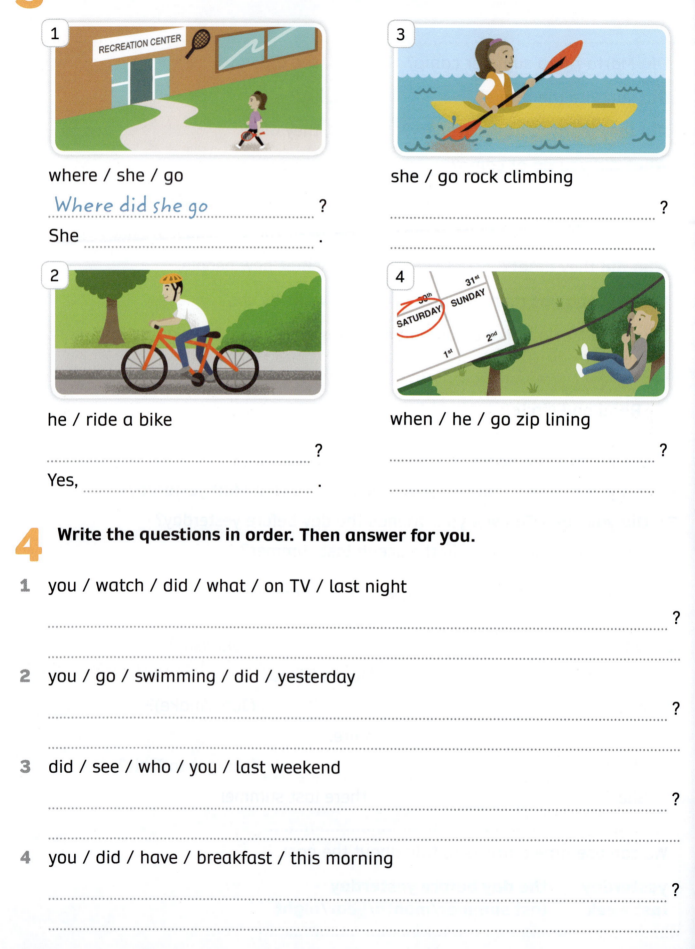

1. where / she / go
Where did she go?
She _____ .

2. he / ride a bike
_____ ?
Yes, _____ .

3. she / go rock climbing
_____ ?
_____ .

4. when / he / go zip lining
_____ ?
_____ .

4 Write the questions in order. Then answer for you.

1 you / watch / did / what / on TV / last night

_____ ?

_____

2 you / go / swimming / did / yesterday

_____ ?

_____

3 did / see / who / you / last weekend

_____ ?

_____

4 you / did / have / breakfast / this morning

_____ ?

_____

42

Writing

1 Write sentences.

on the first day   last week   yesterday   the next day   then

My vacation

¹ .... I went on a short vacation with my family.
² .... , we went to the beach and swam in the ocean. The water was very cold. ³ .... , we went zip lining. It was very exciting and I loved the view. ⁴ .... we had a picnic. We came back home ⁵ .... The vacation was short, but I had a lot of fun.

2 Make notes about a vacation you went on.

1 Who did you go with?

2 How did you get there?

3 What did you see/do?

4 What places did you visit?

5 How did you feel?

6 Why was it a good vacation?

3 Write about your vacation. Use your ideas from Activity 2 to help you.

(!) Remember
1 Write a title.
2 Use paragraphs.
3 Use time phrases.
4 Check spelling.

43

Now I Know

1 Read and correct the words in bold.

1 camping **bag** ....
2 make **up** ....
3 set up **a fire** ....
4 sleeping **stove** ....
5 clean **lost** ....
6 get **a tent** ....

2 Read and write. Use the words from the box.

| beautiful | campsite | compass | flashlight |
| go kayaking | heavy | unsafe | waterfall |

1 Do you have a .... ? I think we're lost.
2 My backpack is very .... I have a lot of books inside.
3 You shouldn't .... on this river. It's ....
4 Look at that butterfly! It's so .... and colorful.
5 Can you give me the .... ? It's dark in here.
6 There's a beautiful .... close to the ....

3 Read and complete. Use the words in parentheses.

Hi Sam!
I'm writing from Kefalonia in Greece! On the first day, we ¹................... (not go) to the swimming pool – we went swimming in the sea. Then we ²................... (have) lunch in a nice restaurant. We ³................... (not eat) dessert there. We ⁴................... (eat) an ice cream at the beach. The next day, we ⁵................... (climb) Mount Aenos – it was amazing. What ⁶................... (you/do) last week?
See you next week!
David

44

4 Read the answers. Then write the questions.

1 Where _____ ?
   We went on vacation to a campsite beside a lake.

2 Who _____ ?
   I went with my parents.

3 When _____ ?
   We went there last summer.

4 What _____ ?
   We went kayaking, fishing, and swimming. It was fun!

5 Look at the pictures. Write what Samir and Safiye did on their vacation.

Things I learn

1 What are your three favorite words in this unit?

2 Write something you think is interesting about:

vacations _____

summer camps _____

3 What kind of vacations do you like? Why?

45

4 Why do we tell stories?

1 What stories do you like reading? Why?

....

....

2 Circle kinds of stories. Then think about and write one thing you learn in this unit.

science fiction   book   adventure   dictionary

....

3   Watch the video. Then look and write.

arrow
bow
costume
forest
target

1 ....
2 ....
3 ....
4 ....
5 ....

4   Read and match. Watch the video again to check.

1 Robin Hood lived
2 The Robin Hood Festival
3 A medieval suit of armor
4 Robin Hood stole from the rich
5 Robin Hood won

a the sheriff's bow and arrow contest.
b in medieval times.
c takes place every year in Sherwood Forest.
d is very heavy.
e and gave to the poor.

46

Vocabulary 1

1 Find and write the words. Then look and match.

A	B	C	D	E	F	G	H	I	J	K	L	M	N	O	P	Q	R	S	T	U	V	W	X	Y	Z
1	2	3	4	5	6	7	8	9	10	11	12	13	14	15	16	17	18	19	20	21	22	23	24	25	26

a ___ ___ ___ ___ ___ ___
   3 1 19 20 12 5

b ___ ___ ___ ___ ___
   7 9 1 14 20

c ___ ___ ___ ___ ___ ___ ___ ___
   6 1 9 18 25 20 1 12 5

d ___ ___ ___ ___ ___ ___
   16 18 9 14 3 5

e ___ ___ ___ ___ ___ ___
   19 9 12 22 5 18

f ___ ___ ___ ___ ___ ___ ___ ___
   5 14 15 18 13 15 21 19

1

2

3

4

5

6

2 Read, choose, and write. Then match.

> bowl   coins   fairy tales   furious   princess

1 Do we have any fruit?
2 How much money do you have?
3 Was your dad angry with you for breaking the window?
4 Who lives in this castle?
5 What stories do you enjoy?

a Yes, he was _____ .
b A beautiful _____ lives there.
d Not very much. I only have a few _____ .
c I really like _____ .
e There are apples in the _____ .

47

3 Think and answer.

1 Who lives in a castle?

2 What's your favorite fairy tale?

Vocabulary challenge: kinds of books

4 Read, choose, and write.

> mystery   non-fiction   realistic fiction   science fiction

1 _____: a story about a detective that must solve a puzzle or a crime

2 _____: a story that can happen in real life

3 _____: a story that often happens in space and has aliens and UFOs

4 _____: a book that gives us facts and tells us how things work

5 Read and circle.

1 Mrs. Gray's cat disappears. No one can find the cat, not even the police. A few days later, Melissa sees the cat on TV! But how did the cat get there and why?

mystery / non-fiction

2 R3B4 is from the planet Zion. He doesn't like Earth because there are no green and blue burgers. He can't go home because his spaceship doesn't work. R3B4 is very sad until he meets John – the boy who knows everything about rockets.

mystery / science fiction

3 Terry is unhappy at school and at home. His parents work long hours and his best friend is mad at him. Terry is so unhappy that he starts missing school. Then his parents find out. What's Terry going to do?

realistic fiction / non-fiction

4 Did you know that whales can sing? Did you know that dolphins and whales are mammals? This book will amaze you and help you understand the animals in our planet's oceans.

non-fiction / science fiction

Reading 1

1 Read the story. What happened to the beans?

Jack and the Beanstalk

Once upon a time there was a boy called Jack. One day his mother said, "Jack, we have no food. We have to sell the cow. Can you take her to market?" On the way to town, Jack met a man. The man said, "I want to buy your cow. Can I give you these magic beans?" So, Jack gave him the cow and took the beans home. His mother was very angry because he didn't go to the market. She threw the beans into the yard.

The next morning, Jack saw a very tall beanstalk in the yard. He climbed up to the sky and saw an enormous castle. Inside, there was a long table with a hen and a golden harp on it.

Suddenly, Jack heard a loud noise and ran into a cupboard to hide. A giant came into the room. "Lay an egg now!" he said. The hen laid an enormous golden egg. "Play me a song!" the giant said. The harp played a beautiful song and the giant fell asleep.

Jack came out of the cupboard and picked up the hen and the harp. The harp stopped playing and the hen started clucking. The giant woke up. He was furious! Jack ran out of the castle and climbed back down the beanstalk. The giant followed him.

When he reached the bottom, Jack shouted, "Mother! Help!" Jack's mother quickly cut down the beanstalk. The giant fell to the ground and died. With the hen's golden eggs and the magic harp, Jack and his mother were rich and lived happily ever after.

2 Read and circle. Are the events in the correct order? If no, number the sentences in order.

1   Jack took the harp and hen and climbed **down / up** the beanstalk.
2   Jack's mother **talked about the hen / cut down the beanstalk**.
3   Next, **the harp played a song / the giant was furious**.
4   When Jack entered the castle, he saw **a long table / a cupboard**.
5   The giant told the hen to **eat his food / lay an egg**.
6   Jack climbed the beanstalk and saw **a castle / a giant**.

3 Imagine you're Jack. Do you steal the hen and harp? Why?

Grammar 1

1 Read and circle action words in the past. Then look and match.

a They saw an Egyptian mummy at the museum.
b We woke up very early and went to the beach.
c My dad made a delicious cake.
d Tom watched an interesting movie.
e We didn't read stories today. We took a test!
f I didn't find my phone. I was very sad.

present	past
come	– came
take	– took
put	– put
get	– got
meet	– met

2 Complete the chart. Then read and complete the sentences with the words in the past.

Present	Past	Present	Past
come		see	
buy		go	
wake up		eat	

1 I .... to the store and .... some ice cream for dessert.
2 We .... home early from the park because it started raining.
3 Yesterday, we .... a movie about penguins.
4 Yang .... too late and missed the bus.
5 Jerry .... all the cookies and his mom was furious.

3 Read and complete. Use the past form of the words in the box. Then match.

| be | be | come | find | go | go | meet | take | wear |

1 Allie and Finn .... coats
2 They .... new people when
3 I .... a shower and
4 Karen .... home late

a I .... to bed.
b because she .... a lost puppy in the street.
c they .... on vacation.
d because it .... cold.

4 Check (✓) the things you did last week. Then write sentences.

wear gloves ✓
meet some new people ☐
buy some candy ☐
take a shower ☐
have ice cream ☐
find something I lost ☐

5 Write sentences about yesterday for you.

1 (wear) Yesterday, I ....
2 (eat) Yesterday, I ....
3 ....
4 ....
5 ....

Vocabulary 2

1 Write the letters in order. Then read and match.

1 g l e n e d ....
2 n e e u q ....
3 h c s a e r ....
4 r e c e f i ....
5 g n i k ....

a a man who rules a country
b angry and scary
c to look for something
d a woman who rules a country
e an old story about adventures

2 Listen and check (✓).

1 Where's the boy?

 a ☐

 b ☐

 c ☐

2 Which movie are the children talking about?

 a ☐

 b ☐

 c ☐

3 What is the girl looking at?

 a ☐

 b ☐

 c ☐

52

3 Look and write two sentences about each picture.

| king   hide   search | queen   husband   fierce |

....

....

....

....

....

Word study: opposites

4 Read, choose, and write. Then write your own.

| early   light   night   noisy   old |

.... – young   .... – heavy   .... – quiet

.... – day   .... – late   .... – ....

5 Read and complete. Use the words from Activity 4.
Then circle the opposites.

1 I can carry .... things. My dad has to carry the **heavy / young** things.
2 My baby cousin is very .... , but our grandpa is very **early / old**.
3 We sleep at .... and we go to school during the **light / day**.
4 We get up .... during the week and **late / quiet** on the weekend.
5 The children are .... in class, but **sad / noisy** on the playground.

53

Reading 2

1 Read the project. Then complete the mind map.

The Legend of Robin Hood

In the past, there weren't any books. People told stories about famous men and women. They told the stories many times and the details changed over time. The stories became legends.

My favourite legend is Robin Hood. It's about a man who lived in Sherwood Forest around 600 years ago. People were sad because the scary Sheriff of Nottingham took all their gold. Robin Hood and his friends, the Merry Men, were very good at using bows and arrows. They lived in the woods. They took gold from those who had too much and gave it to people who had nothing.

Robin's best friend was called Little John, but he wasn't little; he was more than two metres tall! He was very loyal and often helped Robin. He was calm and careful.

Will Scarlet was also a good friend to Robin, but he wasn't calm like Little John. He got angry very easily. He was a good fighter and helped Robin steal gold from the rich.

Robin Hood wanted Maid Marian to be his wife, but Robin had no money, so her uncle didn't want her to marry him. However, Marian visited him in the forest. She wore men's clothes so nobody knew who she was. In the end, she became his wife.

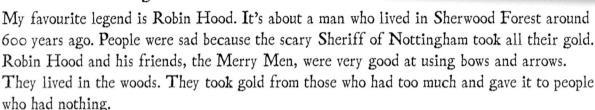

very tall

2 Read and check (✔) the correct sentences.

1 Robin Hood and the sheriff were good friends. ☐
2 Little John was over two meters tall. ☐
3 Will Scarlet helped Robin steal from a princess. ☐

3 💡 Why is it important to help our friends?

....

Grammar 2

Who **was** that? | What **did** you **do**? | **What happened**?
What was that? | Where **did** she **go**? | **Who believed** in gods and goddesses?
Who **were** they? | When **did** she **arrive**? | **Who had** a myth about a sleeping giant?
Where **were** the people? | Who **did** he **ask**? |

1 Read and circle.

1 Who **be** / **were** / **was** the bad character in Robin Hood?
2 Why did you **hides** / **hide** / **hid** under the bed?
3 What did you **ate** / **eat** / **eats** in the morning?
4 Where did you **find** / **found** / **finds** this information?
5 Who **come** / **did come** / **came** to see you?

2 Read and complete the questions. Then match.

1 What _____ (they/make) for lunch?
2 Who _____ (live) in Greece?
3 Why _____ (Tony/wear) a coat?
4 Where _____ (Anna and Pete/be)?

a My cousins lived there.
b He wore a coat because it was cold.
c They were at the bookstore.
d They made a salad.

3 Read the answers. Then complete the questions.

1 What did Joe _____ to the party?
Joe wore a nice blue shirt and jeans.
2 Where did Josie _____ Max?
She saw Max on the playground.
3 Why _____ your parents at school?
They were at school because they had a meeting with my teacher.

4 Read and complete the questions. Use the past form of the words in the box. Then answer the questions.

find   have   wake up   wear

1
What time .... yesterday?
She .... at ....

3
Why .... a party?
He .... a party because it was his ....

2
Where .... the shell?
They .... the shell at the ....

4
Who .... a scary costume?
.... a scary costume.

5 Write the questions in order. Then answer for you.

1 you / did / what / do / last night

....?
....

2 you / go / where / did / last summer

....?
....

3 see / you / did / who / on the weekend

....?
....

4 did / learn / when / you / to swim

....?
....

Writing

1 Read and circle the reasons why Adam likes King Arthur.

King Arthur

I love reading legends and myths from around the world. My favorite are legends about King Arthur. He was brave and strong. He pulled a sword from a stone and this proved that he should be the king. He lived in a castle called Camelot.

King Arthur was a great fighter and he had a famous sword called Excalibur. I like him because he and his knights helped others.

2 Read and make notes about your favorite character.

1 What's his/her name?

2 What do you like about your character

3 What does he/she do in the story?

4 Write three words that describe him/her.

3 Write about your character. Use your ideas from Activity 2 to help you.

(!) Remember
1 Write a title.
2 Use paragraphs.
3 Give simple reasons for your opinions.
4 Check spelling.

57

Now I Know

1 Read and circle **T** (true) or **F** (false).

1. An enormous tree is very small. T F
2. A queen's husband is called a king. T F
3. To visit a castle, you have to travel in time. T F
4. A hero is a person who helps people. T F
5. A legend is a story about today. T F

2 Read and circle.

1. The Ugly Duckling is my favorite **princess** / **fairy tale** / **giant**.
2. I think **fierce** / **legends** / **husbands** about heroes are very interesting.
3. My brother's **castle** / **prince** / **wife** is very nice. Her name's Trish.
4. Jimmy always eats my candy. I have to **search** / **hide** / **furious** it from him.
5. My favorite **bowl** / **coin** / **myth** is blue. I always eat my cereal in it.

3 Find and circle eight words in the past. Then look and complete.

omtookowokepfounddfworeawonprannsaidnhgot

Alfredo _____ the race.

James _____ a coin in the sand.

Brieanne _____ a crown and a beautiful dress.

The thieves _____ our TV.

4 Read and complete.

1 How _____ to China? He went to China by plane.
2 What did your parents give you? My parents _____ me money.
3 What _____ at summer camp? We went zip lining and kayaking.
4 Where did you find the pen? I _____ it in my backpack.
5 Why did you buy him a gift? I _____ him a gift because it was his birthday.
6 What _____ in France? I saw many cool places. I really liked the Louvre.

5 Write sentences. Use the words you didn't use in Activity 3.

Things I learn

1 What are your three favorite words in this unit?

....

2 Write something you think is interesting about:

fairy tales ....

myths and legends ....

3 What kind of stories do you like to tell and read? Why?

....

....

59

5 Why take care of the environment?

1 Who can help the environment? Write two things you do to help the environment.

....

....

2 Circle the things that are bad for the environment. Then think about and write one thing you learn in this unit.

pollution   recycling   deforestation   trash   hunting

....

3 Watch the video. Look, choose, and write. Then write *N* (noise pollution) or *A* (air pollution).

factories   loud music   shouting   traffic

1   2   3   4

....

4 Read and check (✓) the correct sentences. Watch the video again to check.

1 Noise pollution wakes people up. ☐
2 Music helps people sleep. ☐
3 Air pollution is good for plants. ☐
4 Riding bikes and walking are good for the environment. ☐

Vocabulary 1

1 Write the letters in order. Then look and match.

1 s u c r e e ....
2 t t a b i h a ....
3 u n r y t c o ....
4 d w l i e l i f ....
5 n a t l p ....
6 s t c e n i ....
7 t y t r e p ....
8 l u l f ....
9 w r o h t y a a w ....
10 e s h r f i r a ....

2 Read and complete. Use the words from the box.

Zebras don't live in the country. Their natural ¹ _habitat_ is the savannah in Africa. Not many ² .... grow there because it's very dry. However, there are a lot of ³ .... like flies and mosquitoes. There are also many other kinds of ⁴ .... , such as lions, elephants, and giraffes. Zebras are my favorite animals.

insects | habitat | throw away
plants | full | wildlife

61

3 Think and write.

1 Why do people enjoy long walks in the country?
....

2 What isn't there a lot of in the city?
....

3 What should you do when you see trash on the ground?
....

Word study: phrases with *cut*

4 Look, read, and circle.

cut away   cut down   cut out   cut up

1 You should cut **out** / **away** the dry leaves of plants so they can grow better.
2 My Mom cuts **up** / **down** my old T-shirts to make dish towels.
3 I cut **up** / **out** pictures I like from magazines and use them to decorate my bedroom.
4 My parents want to cut **up** / **down** the old tree in our yard because it's getting too big.

5 Think and write.

Name things ...
1 you can cut away ....
2 you shouldn't cut down ....
3 you can cut up ....
4 you can cut out ....

62

Reading 1

1 Read the story. Stop after the questions in bold and guess the answers.

Balloons

"Three … two … one … go!" said the man, and hundreds of balloons flew up from the park into the air above.
The balloons all had the number 200 on them because today the town is 200 years old.
Abbie and Josh looked at the balloons happily.
"They look pretty," said Abbie. "But where are they going?"
"To Britain," said Josh, "or to China! Sometimes balloons fly a very long way."
"Do the balloons land in the forest? **Can they hurt the animals?**" said Abbie.

On their way home Abbie and Josh passed the forest. They saw burst balloons in the trees and they heard the birds screaming. Some were tangled in the strings and rubber!

"You were right, Abbie. Poor birds," said Josh. **"What can we do to help?"**

Abbie had an idea. She called the fire department, and later she and Josh took pictures of the rescue action. That night, they wrote a blog about the balloons and the birds.

The next day, Josh woke Abbie up very early. "Come and look, Abbie!" They ran downstairs. The mayor of their town was on TV. "I'm very sorry for letting the balloons go up in the air," said the mayor. "Thank you to Abbie and Josh for their blog post and for showing us how dangerous balloons can be for wildlife."

2 Read and complete.

1 Abbie was worried about the _____ in the forest.
2 The birds were _____ because they got tangled.
3 A lot of people read Abbie and Josh's _____ .
4 The blog helped save the wildlife in the forest from more _____ .

3 Why is it important to protect wildlife?

Grammar 1

> It's **safer** in the TARDIS.
> The Doctor was **happier** before the plant caught him.
> We need to be **quicker**.
> We were **slower than** the Smogator.
> The Smogator is **bigger than** us.

1 Circle the word that compares things. Underline the word that follows it. Then match.

1 Tom is (drier) than Jenny.
2 A tiger is smaller than an elephant.
3 A snake is longer than a worm.
4 The clown is funnier than the vet.
5 Brazil is larger than Peru.
6 Lily is sadder than Rose.

2 Read and circle.

1 The country is **quieter** / **quiet** than the city.
2 I think chocolate is **tasty** / **tastier** than cookies.
3 A castle is **big** / **bigger** than an apartment.
4 In winter, Canada is usually **cold** / **colder** than Mexico.
5 A car is **faster** / **fast** than a bike.
6 The air in the city is **dirtier** / **dirty** than in the country.

It's a **good** habitat for wildlife. It's **better** than other kinds of field.

The rules here are really **bad**. They're **worse** than the rules at school!

What **a lot** of insects! There are **more** here than in the school.

3 Read and complete. Use the correct form of the words in parentheses.

1 I'm _____ (good) at math than science.
2 The old campsite is _____ (bad) than the new one.
3 China is _____ (big) than Germany.
4 My little sister is _____ (short) than me.

4 Look and compare the pictures. Use the correct form of the words from the box.

> dirty   happy   wet

1 The rain forest is ___*wetter than the forest*___ .
2 _____
3 _____

5 Compare your town/city to another one you know. Use the words from the box.

> big   busy   clean   dirty   noisy   pretty   quiet   small

65

Vocabulary 2

1 Find and circle nine words. The remaining letters form an extra word. What is it?

pgadgetsooilweprotectrcoalpburnllungsafossilfuelnelectricitytbreathe

The extra word is: .... It's ....

2 Read and complete. Use the words from Activity 1.

1 We use .... for the lights and TV in our homes.
2 These days, most people have .... like smartphones and tablets.
3 .... spills destroy our oceans and sea life.
4 .... is a hard, black rock. People burn it to make energy.
5 We use our .... to breathe.

3 Look and write. Then use the words to complete the text.

AIR POLLUTION

Gas, [1] ...., and [2] .... are kinds of [3] .... We find them deep inside the Earth and they're millions of years old. They come from dead animals and plants. [4] .... use fossil fuels to produce electricity. However, when they [5] .... fossil fuels, they send dangerous gases and chemicals into the air. This means the air we [6] .... is dirty and polluted. The second problem is that there isn't much fossil fuel left. This is why we should use other forms of energy.

4 Read, think, and write.

1 Three things we can burn: ....
2 Three things which use electricity: ....
3 Three things we should protect: ....
4 Three gadgets that you have at home: ....

Vocabulary challenge: kinds of renewable energy

5 Look and read. Then circle the kinds of energy your town uses.

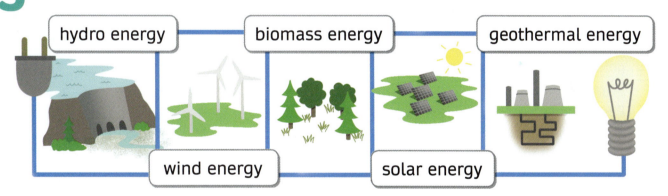

6 Read and write. Use the words from Activity 5.

1 We use the energy from the sun to make water warm and to make electricity.
   ....

2 Plants and animal waste are turned into fuel. This is the oldest form of renewable energy. ....

3 We use the energy from falling or fast-moving water to make electricity.
   ....

4 We use the warmth that comes from deep in the earth to make electricity and warm our homes ....

5 Strong winds turn the windmill's arms. This helps a small box inside the windmill make electricity. ....

67

Reading 2

1 Read *Deforestation* and underline the sentences you don't understand. Then read the underlined sentences again, and the parts before or after. Does this help you understand?

DEFORESTATION

The world's forests are very important. Trees make oxygen, and without oxygen we can't breathe. So why do we cut down an area of forest bigger than 20 football pitches every minute? We should protect our trees, not cut them down.

Why do people cut down trees?
There are more people in the world now than ever before. All those people need food and houses. People cut down forests to make space for bigger farms so we can produce more food. They also cut down forests to make space for buildings, and they use the wood to build houses.

What are the effects of deforestation?
Trees turn bad air into oxygen, so when we cut them down we haven't got as much fresh air to breathe. Also, 70 percent of Earth's animals and plants live in forests. Without their food or habitat, animals and plants cannot live. Trees also protect us from the sun, wind and rain. With fewer trees, the Earth gets hotter and there are more floods.

What can we do?
Paper comes from trees. If we use paper carefully, and reuse and recycle our paper, we can help save more trees. Teaching people about the effects of deforestation is really important too. We should also plant as many trees as possible.

2 Read the leaflet again. Circle **T** (true) or **F** (false).

1 Forests get smaller so that farms can get bigger.   T   F
2 A small number of animals live in forests.   T   F
3 Animals and plants die because of deforestation.   T   F
4 Trees make the Earth hotter.   T   F

3 Think and write. What two things can you do to help stop deforestation?

....

....

68

Grammar 2

> These bees are **the biggest** and **ugliest** on Earth.
> Air pollution is one of **the worst** problems for the environment.
> **The best** cars for the environment are electric cars.
> Which country cuts down **the most** trees?

1 Read and match.

1 I have the smallest   a cake. No wonder he's sick.
2 John ate the most   b worst. I don't understand anything!
3 The park is   c bedroom in our house.
4 This movie is the   d the cleanest place in our neighborhood.

2 Read and choose.

1 Who's **tall** / **the taller** / **the tallest** person in your family?
2 Alejandro is **smarter than** / **the smartest** / **the smarter** student in his class.
3 Jenny makes **the best** / **better than** / **best** carrot cake in the world!
4 Where's **the higher** / **higher than** / **the highest** mountain in the world?
5 Selen is **the happier** / **the happiest** / **the happy** person I know.
6 My mom's grandpa is **the oldest** / **older than** / **oldest than** person in our family. He's 101!

3 Read and complete. Use the correct form of the words in parentheses.

1 Walking is _____ (good) for the environment than taking a bus.
2 Gina is _____ (nice) friend I have.
3 A lion's roar is _____ (loud) than a bird's chirp.
4 I hate fish. They have _____ (bad) smell!
5 My cousins are _____ (noisy) than my brothers.
6 What's _____ (big) rain forest in the world?

69

4 Look, read, and write sentences.

Weston

Easton

Southon

1 (quiet) *Southon is the quietest town.*
2 (dirty) ....
3 (clean) ....
4 (busy) ....
5 (good place to live) ....
6 (bad place to live) ....

5 Write the questions. Then answer for you.

1 Who's / short / person in your family
....?
....

2 Where's / quiet / place in your neighborhood
....?
....

3 What's / nice / place in your town
....?
....

4 What's / fast / way to get to your school
....?
....

5 Who's / good / sports person in the world
....?
....

70

Writing

1 Read and write. Use the words from the box.

> conclusion   information   introduction

PROTECT CORAL REEFS

1 ....

For these reasons, we must protect our coral reefs. We need to stop polluting our oceans with chemicals and trash. Together, we can save the coral reefs!

2 ....

Coral reefs are home to one quarter of the Earth's sea animals and plants. Corals look like rocks, but they're actually polyps. They're very fragile. If people or boats touch them, they die. Pollution can also damage them.

3 ....

This damage means that coral reefs are slowly dying. Many animals and plants need coral reefs to survive. They also help clean the ocean and protect the land from big waves.

2 Read and make notes for your leaflet.

1 What's the topic?

....

2 What's the title?

....

3 What problems are there?

....

4 What can we do to help?

....

3 Write your leaflet. Use your ideas from Activity 2 to help you.

(!) Remember

1 Write a title.
2 Write an introduction and a conclusion.
3 Give more information.
4 Use paragraphs.

Now I Know

1 Look and circle.

breathe
country

full
insect

coal
oil

fresh air
lungs

plant
habitat

wildlife
pretty

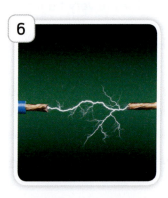
power plant
electricity

fossil fuel
gadget

2 Read and complete. Use the words from the box. Then match.

> breathe   fossil fuels   power plants
> pretty   protect   throw away

1 We can _____ because
2 Coal and oil are _____ .
3 _____ produce electricity,
4 It's so _____ here!
5 We have to _____
6 Don't _____ paper

a They come from under the ground.
b we have lungs.
c Look at the flowers!
d because we can recycle it.
e but they pollute the air.
f our environment.

72

3 Read and write sentences. Use the words in parentheses.

	Height	Hobbies	Personality	Family
Claire	130 cm	softball, soccer	loud	3 brothers
Tony	145 cm	reading	quiet	1 sister

1 (tall) Tony is taller than Claire.
2 (busy) ......
3 (quiet) ......
4 (big family) ......

4 Write true sentences.

1 tortoises / live / elephants / long
......

2 giraffes / lions / tall
......

3 Russia / large / country / world
......

Things I learn

1 What are your three favorite words in this unit?

......

2 Write something you think is interesting about:

helping animals ......
deforestation ......

3 What's the best thing we can do to help the environment?

......

73

6 Why do we use numbers every day?

1 How do we use numbers in our daily lives? Write two ways numbers help you.

....

....

2 Circle the activities for which you use numbers. Then think about and write one thing you learn in this unit.

checking the time   listening to music   making a cake
playing video games   shopping   washing the dishes

....

3   Watch the video. Then look, read, and write.

¹ This is a ....

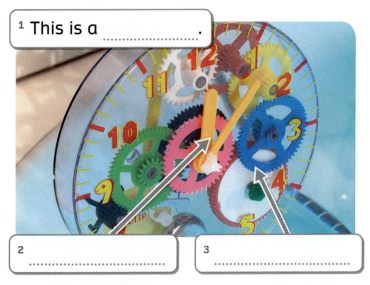

| clock | cogs | hands |
| speeds | turn |

The hands in the clock go at different ⁴ .... to tell us the time. All cogs inside the clock ⁵ .... , but some move faster and some slower.

2 ....   3 ....

4 Read and circle. Watch the video again to check.

1 The cogs are **inside / outside** a clock.
2 The small hand moves the **fastest / slowest** of all three hands.
3 The cogs in a clock are **the same / different** sizes.
4 Big cogs move **faster / slower** than small cogs.
5 The hands of a clock **tell the time / move the cogs**.

Vocabulary 1

1 Read and check (✔) the correct picture.

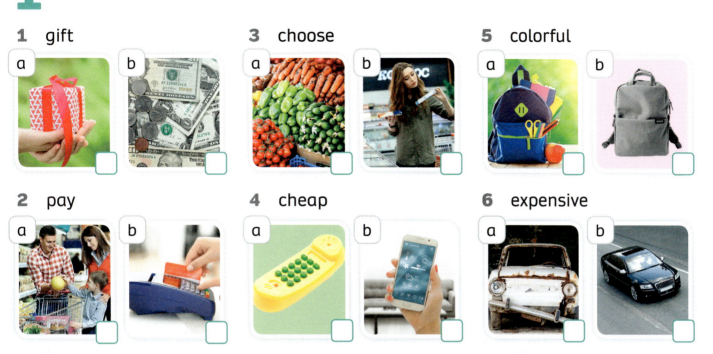

2 Read and complete. Use the words from the box. There are two extra words.

> cheap   chose   colorful   expensive   gifts
> go shopping   money   pay   stall   useful

Friday, March 2nd

Today I had to ¹……………………… with my mom to buy ²……………………… for my dad's birthday. Mom bought him a GPS. It's ³……………………… because Dad travels a lot and needs a map. Now he has his GPS to help him. Mom didn't have any cash so she had to ⁴……………………… with her credit card. I ⁵……………………… a sweater from a market ⁶……………………… . It's red, blue, green, and orange – very ⁷……………………… . I bought it with the pocket ⁸……………………… I save every week.

75

3 Write the letters in order. Then choose four words and write sentences.

1 p e x n i v e s e .... 4 l u f o o l r c ....
2 l u f e s u .... 5 p e a c h ....
3 o s o e c h .... 6 l l s a t ....

Vocabulary challenge: forms of payment

4 Look, choose, and write.

bills   cash   coins   credit card   gift card

1 ....
2 ....
3 ....
4 ....
5 ....

5 Read and circle.

Money, money, money!

Did you know … ?

- The largest dollar ¹ **bill / coin** today in the U.S. is $100. But in 1934, they printed one worth $100,000!
- These days, only 8 percent of the money in the world is ² **cash / gift cards**. The rest is "digital money" – it only exists on computers.
- In the U.S., you have to be 18 years old to get a ³ **credit card / bill**.
- People first started using ⁴ **credit cards / coins** to buy things in 700 B.C.
- In 2016, people in the U.S. spent $46 billion on ⁵ **gift cards / coins**.

Reading 1

1 Does Ethan like going shopping? Read and check.
Do you like going shopping?

GROCERY STORE ADVENTURE

"Why do we have to go shopping every Saturday?" said Ethan. "Grocery stores are boring."
But Ethan's mom didn't listen.
"Come on!" she said with a smile. "Let's get in the car."
"Can we buy ice cream?" asked Saskia, Ethan's little sister. She loved going to the grocery store and choosing her favorite food.
"Yes, we can. And Ethan can choose a box of cookies, too."

Still, Ethan wasn't very happy. He didn't like the music and the noise in the grocery store.
"Look, Ethan! Your favorite cookies," said Saskia. Ethan didn't look at Saskia or the cookies. He watched a man in a big black coat behind them. He saw the man put bags of candy under his coat.
"Help! Thief!" Ethan shouted very loudly.
The man started running. Bags of chips and boxes of cereal were falling out of his pockets and from under his coat.

Suddenly, the man tripped.
"That man is a thief! Call the police!", yelled Ethan as the store guard showed up.
The police arrived very quickly and arrested the thief. A police officer thanked Ethan.
"Good job! You're very brave," he said.
"I think you deserve two boxes of cookies today!" said Ethan's mom.
"Yes!" said the store owner. "And from now on, Ethan can have a free box of cookies when he comes shopping with you."
"Um, I'm afraid Ethan doesn't like shopping," said Ethan's mom.
"I do now!" said Ethan.

2 Read the text again and answer the questions.

1 What didn't Ethan like about the grocery store?
2 What was the thief wearing?
3 What did the man try to steal?
4 How does the grocery store owner thank Ethan?

3 Ethan shouts loudly and calls for help. Was this the right thing to do? Why?

Grammar 1

1 Can we please open that **box of** cookies? c
2 I'd like **a** new **pair of** sandals. d
3 Can I have **a piece of** cake? f b
4 I want to buy that **pack of** pencils. a
5 There's **a bag of** grapes in the fridge. e c f
6 I ate **a bar of** chocolate. b

1 Read and complete. Use the words from the box.

| bag | bar | box | pack | pair | piece |

1 a .... of chips, tomatoes, candy
2 a .... of soap, chocolate
3 a .... of pasta, rice
4 a .... of jeans, socks, shoes
5 a .... of cereal, crayons, chocolates
6 a .... of cake, fruit, pie

2 Look, read, and write. Use the words from Activity 1.

1 Would you like *a bar of chocolate* ?

2 Can I have .... ?

3 We need to buy .... The old ones are too small.

4 There's .... on the table.

5 I bought .... at the grocery store.

6 Do you have another .... ? This one is empty.

3 Look, read, and complete.

Today Mom and I went to the store. We bought
¹ *two boxes of* .... Dad's favorite cookies and
three ² .... to make my favorite
cake. We also got ³ .... watermelon
and four ⁴ .... for my lunch box this
week. Mom also bought ⁵ ....
for herself and four ⁶ .... for
me and my sisters, because we like to draw a lot.

4 Write a plan for your next birthday. Use some of the phrases and words from the boxes.

| a bag of | a bar of | a box of | a pack of | a pair of | a piece of |

| balloons | candles | candy | chips | chocolate cookies |
| headphones | jeans | party hats | pens | shoes |

My Birthday plan

Date: ....

Food:
I need two bags
of chips ...

Decorations:

Presents:

79

Vocabulary 2

1 Read and circle. Then look and match.

1 Someone ate a **shadow** / **quarter** of the pizza!
2 I'm late! My class starts in 15 **hours** / **minutes**.
3 I couldn't **tell the time** / **invent** because the old clock didn't work.
4 My uncle likes **inventing** / **telling** things.
5 I was so thirsty that I drank **hour** / **half** a bottle of water.

 a  b  c  d  e

2 Read and circle T (true) or F (false).

1 A second is longer than three minutes.   T   F
2 An hour is longer than 45 minutes.   T   F
3 A decade is longer than a century.   T   F
4 A quarter is the same as a half.   T   F
5 A century is 100 years.   T   F
6 You can see your shadow when it's sunny.   T   F

3 Read and complete. Use the words from the box.

| hours   invent   minutes   seconds   tell the time |

1 There are 60 _____ in one minute.
2 One hour is 60 _____ .
3 There are 24 _____ in a day.
4 I want to _____ a robot that cleans up.
5 My little sister can't _____ . I have to look at the clock and tell her.

80

4 Circle the odd one out. Then write sentences with the words you circled.

1	quarter	half	shadow
2	invent	decade	tell the time
3	decade	century	second
4	half	hour	minute

Word study: sounds

5 Read these word aloud. Then match.

decade   hour   time

1 aʊ: ....   2 eɪ: ....   3 aɪ: ....

6 Find and circle six words. Use the words to complete the chart. Then write one more word in each column.

hythousepnslightdrutailtsuwildlifekcgypowerskutakewqy

aʊ	eɪ	aɪ

81

Reading 2

1 Read the text and write the times.

Dakar *12 p.m.*

Vancouver ....

Karachi ....

Honolulu ....

Sydney ....

Lima ....

Auckland ....

Time Around the World

The Earth is constantly spinning around, but it completes one rotation around its axis about every 24 hours. The Sun is always in the sky above half of the Earth, but in the other half of the Earth, it's night.

What time is it?

In **Dakar**, Senegal, it's midday and children are starting their lunch break. But it's not the same everywhere. **Lima**, Peru, is five hours behind Dakar time. It's seven o'clock in the morning there, and children are getting up. In **Vancouver**, Canada, it's only 3 a.m., and most people are still fast asleep. In **Karachi**, Pakistan, it's five o'clock in the afternoon – people are relaxing after a long day at school and work. In **Sydney**, Australia, it's now 11 o'clock at night, and most children are already asleep.

What day is it?

The dates around the world are also different. When it's 11 o'clock on Monday morning in **Honolulu**, Hawaii, it's nine o'clock on Tuesday morning in **Auckland**, New Zealand. Between these two places, in the middle of the Pacific Ocean, is the **International Date Line**. It isn't a real line. We mark it on maps to help us know the time and date in different parts of the world. It isn't straight because countries can choose which date and time zone they want to be in.

2 Read and complete the sentences with one word.

1 When it's day in one half of the world, it's .... in the other half.
2 The International Date Line is in the middle of the .... Ocean.
3 The International Date Line isn't a real line, it's marked on ....

3 When is it useful to know what time and day it is in different parts of the world?

....

82

Grammar 2

What's the time?

 It's eight o'clock.

 It's eight thirty.

 It's quarter after eight.

 It's quarter till nine.

 eight

 eight fifteen

08:30 eight thirty

08:45 eight forty-five

1 Look, read, and check (✓).

1 It's six fifteen. ☐
It's six thirty. ☐

3 It's eleven thirty. ☐
It's quarter till twelve. ☐

2 It's ten fifteen. ☐
 It's ten o'clock. ☐

4 It's quarter after eleven. ☐
 It's eleven forty-five. ☐

2 Read and draw.

1 It's quarter till five.

2 It's four thirty.

3 It's six o'clock.

3 Read and match.

1 eight   a eight forty-five
2 quarter after six   b eight o'clock
3 quarter till nine   c quarter after three
4 three fifteen   d six fifteen

83

4 🎧 📋 **Listen and check (✓).**

1 What time did John wake up?

    8:15   8:45   7:30

    a ☐   b ☐   c ☐

2 What time is it now?

    9:00   10:00   11:00

    a ☐   b ☐   c ☐

3 What did Patricia do at 6:45?

    a ☐   b ☐   c ☐

5 **Look at Tom's schedule. Then read and complete in words.**

Monday:
come home – 4:00
go swimming – 4:45
do homework – 6:30
have dinner – 8:15
watch TV – 9:30
go to bed – 10:15

On Monday, Tom came home at ¹ *four o'clock* .
He went swimming at ² _____ .
After that he did his homework at
³ _____ . At ⁴ _____
he had dinner, and then at ⁵ _____
he watched his favorite show on TV. He went to bed
at ⁶ _____ .

6 **What time did you do these activities yesterday? Write sentences for you.**

1 (wake up) I woke up at _____ .
2 (go to school) _____
3 (go to bed) _____

84

Writing

1 Read and complete. Use the words from the box.

> At   First   in the afternoon   in the morning   Then

My Day at School

I start school at half past nine. [1] .... we have an hour of math [2] .... and then we do P.E. After that we have recess at a quarter after eleven. [3] .... we have two more hours of classes: science, art, music, or history. Art is always really fun! [4] .... a quarter till two we have lunch. I usually have a sandwich and a bag of apple slices. We go home at four o'clock [5] ....

2 Read and make notes about your typical school day.

1 What subjects do you do?

....

2 What time do you start school?

....

3 What time do you have lunch?

....

4 What time does school finish?

....

3 Write about a typical day for your school website. Use your ideas from Activity 2 to help you.

(!) Remember
1 Write a title.
2 Use time words.
3 Use paragraphs.
4 Check your spelling.

85

Now I Know

1 Look and complete the crossword.

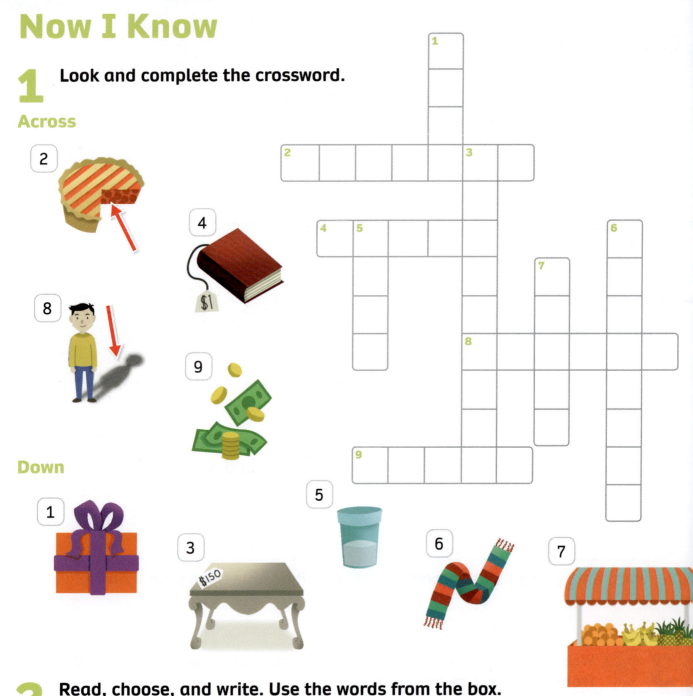

2 Read, choose, and write. Use the words from the box.

| century | decade | invent | minute | pay | useful |

1 It's when you make something new that didn't exist before. ....
2 This is what you call something that helps you. ....
3 It's when you give money to buy something. ....
4 100 years is this. ....
5 It's a word for 10 years. ....
6 It has 60 seconds. ....

3 Look, read, and complete.

Shopping list
1 1 .... of potatoes ✔
2 .... boxes of .... ✔
3 .... of soap ✔
4 .... of socks ✔
5 2 .... of .... ✔
6 .... ✔

4 Look and write what the children did. What time did they do it?

1

2

....
....

Things I learn

1 What are your three favorite words in this unit?

....

2 Write something you think is interesting about:

how we use numbers ....
clocks ....

3 When is it useful for you to know the date and time?

....

87

7 What do we do for entertainment?

1 Why is entertainment important in our lives? Write two things you and your family do for entertainment.

....

....

2 Circle the words we use to talk about good entertainment. Then think about and write one thing you learn in this unit.

laughter   boring   fun   sad   interesting   exciting

....

3 Watch the video. Then look and write.

brass   percussion   string   woodwind

.... instruments   .... instruments   .... instruments   .... instruments

4   Read and write. Watch the video again to check.

B = brass   P = percussion   S = string   W = woodwind

1 You blow into these instruments to make music.   ....
2 A violin and a cello are this kind of instrument.   ....
3 They are usually made of wood.   ....
4 A saxophone is this kind of instrument.   ....
5 You hit these instruments with a stick to make music.   ....

88

Vocabulary 1

1 Look and label the pictures.

> band   hang out   headphones   modern   musician   traditional

1 ....
2 ....
3 ....
4 ....
5 ....
6 ....

2 Read and choose.

1 My friends and I play **chess / headphones / musician** every weekend.
2 Mike wants to be a **musician / chess / band** in a pop **musician / band / magazine** when he grows up.
3 Sara is **afraid / famous / modern** of spiders.

3 Write the letters in order. Then complete the sentences.

1 s s e h c   ....
2 a z i m n e g a ....
3 m s o u f a   ....
4 f r a a i d   ....

a She's .... of the dark. So am I!
b There's a statue of a .... king outside the palace.
c Do you buy this .... every month?
d .... is a difficult game. I can't play it at all!

89

4 **What do you usually do when you hang out with friends? Draw and write two sentences.**

Word study: phrases with *hang*

5 Read the definitions. Then look and complete.

hang around: spend time in a place
hang on: wait for a short time
hang onto: keep something
hang together: help each other

1
.... a minute.
Did we pack everything we need?

2
We should .... these books, we might need them.

3
Timmy and Olivia always
.... It's so sweet.

4
I .... the park with my friends every Saturday.

6 **Think and write.**

1 Where do you hang around?

....

2 What do you hang onto?

....

Reading 1

1 Read the story. What dangerous things happened because of Karen?

A DANGEROUS MORNING

Karen usually listens to music on her way to school. Yesterday, she had her headphones on, as usual. She didn't look, and she almost walked into the road, in front of a car. The driver stopped suddenly, and he hit his head. He shouted at Karen and waved his arms. Karen jumped back onto the pavement and almost knocked down a man standing on a ladder and cleaning windows. "Oi!" shouted the man. "Watch out!"

"Oops! Sorry!" Karen called out.

As Karen arrived at school, she heard the bell ringing. She ran up the stairs and turned toward the music room door. At that same moment, Mrs Jones arrived at the door carrying a pile of books and a cup of tea. As Karen bumped into her, the books fell on the floor and the tea wobbled dangerously in the cup.

"Sorry, Mrs Jones." said Karen as she picked up the books.

"I'm not happy with you at all, Karen. You must think about the consequences of your actions."

"Consequences? What are 'consequences'?"

"Consequences are things that happen as a result of something else," explained Mrs Jones. "For example, because you were late, you ran to class and crashed into me!"

Karen thought about everything she did that morning and felt very bad. She looked around the classroom. There was only one empty desk at the back of the room next to her best friend. "At least not all consequences are bad," she thought.

2 Read the story again. Then complete.

Cause:

Karen jumped back onto the pavement

2 ....

Karen was the last student to arrive.

Effect:

1 ....

She crashed into Mrs. Jones.

3 ....

3 Think about the things you did this week. Write about one action that had good consequences and one action that had bad consequences.

....

....

Grammar 1

She's **interested in** comic books.

I'm **interested in** learn**ing** to play chess.

I'm **bored with** play**ing** video games.

interested in   surprised at
happy with   bored with
afraid of   tired of
worried about

1 Read and match.

1 We're afraid
2 Our parents were very happy
3 The people in the town are worried
4 Do you ever get bored

a about the pollution.
b with listening to that band?
c of snakes.
d with our good grades.

2 Read and complete. Then match.

1 Toby and Fiona are very interested .... science.
2 The children are afraid .... the dark forest.
3 Luke and Marty are tired .... cleaning their room.
4 They're surprised .... their presents.
5 Mara is really happy .... her new bike.
6 Gina is worried .... the test.

a

c

e

b

d

f

3 Complete the sentences with the correct form of the words from the box.

> clean   come   learn   miss   walk

1 Are you interested in .... to my house for dinner?
2 Are you afraid of .... home in the dark?
3 I'm tired of .... your mess!
4 Riley is worried about .... his bus because he got up late.
5 I'm interested in .... more about dinosaurs. Could you lend me a book?

4 Write the questions in order. Then answer for you.

1 which / you / are / of / afraid / animals

....?

....

2 you / are / which / interested / sports / in

....?

....

3 about / you / problems / which / worried / are

....?

....

4 toys or games / with / bored / are / which / you

....?

....

5 which / you / with / are / happy / school subjects

....?

....

Vocabulary 2

1 Look at the pictures and complete the sentences.

1. My cousin can play the ....

3. Azra is learning to play the ....

5. I met my favorite actor. It was so ....!

2. Daniel has difficulty playing the ....

4. I had a great .... last night – I could fly!

6. My cello has four ....

2 Complete the words. Then read and match.

1 c __ l __ __
2 __ r __ __
3 __ l __ r __ __ __ t
4 __ r __ m
5 __ __ c __ __ __ __ __ a
6 s __ x __ p __ __ n __
7 s __ __ __ n __

a a large group of musicians who play together
b a long, woodwind musical instrument that you blow into
c an instrument that looks like a big violin
d a round instrument that you hit with a stick or your hand
e something that you imagine in your mind when you're sleeping or thinking
f the long thin thing that you touch on a violin or a guitar to make music
g a large brass instrument often used in jazz music

3 Think and write.

1 What instruments do people in an orchestra usually play?

....

2 What instruments do people in a band usually play?

....

Vocabulary challenge: kinds of music

4 Look and complete the crossword.

| classical | country | hip hop | jazz | pop | rock |

Across

Down

5 Complete for you.

My favorite kind of music is ....

To make this music people play ....

I'd like to learn to play the ....

Reading 2

1 Read the text. Underline one sentence in each paragraph that is NOT about video games.

Good Sides of Video Games

How many hours do you spend playing video games in a normal week?

A study says that many nine-year-olds play them for more than four hours a week. There are a lot of different games, including games that let you build your own world or play online with friends. Young people play video games a lot, but older people don't. Older people spend their time on the computer watching videos or looking for information on the internet.

Playing video games can be bad for us, but does it help us with anything? Actually, yes!

Playing video games can make you more confident. It's because when you win a level, you feel happy and proud. Winning makes people feel good.

Video games help you practice critical thinking skills. If you're not quick enough, you lose. Making quick decisions is useful in real life as well.

Video games also bring families together because they often need two or more players. Having fun together is a good way for families to bond. Video games are also a good way for children to learn to take turns and not to give up when they lose.

That doesn't mean you should spend hours in front of the screen. It's important to find enough time to get some exercise and have fun outside – every day! So, remember, it's OK to play video games. You can even play every day, but not for too long!

2 Read the text again. Circle **T** (true) or **F** (false).

1. Children spend less time playing video games than adults.   T   F
2. Video games can give you confidence.   T   F
3. If you think quickly, you lose the game.   T   F
4. It's important to exercise every day.   T   F

3 Why is it important to spend time outside and do exercise?

....

Grammar 2

bigger than   the biggest
more interesting than   the most interesting

1 Read and write *more* or *most*.

1 My sister's bike is .... expensive than mine.
2 My parents' bedroom is the .... beautiful room in our house.
3 My scarf is .... colorful than my friend's scarf.
4 I think rock climbing is the .... exciting sport.

2 Read, choose, and write.

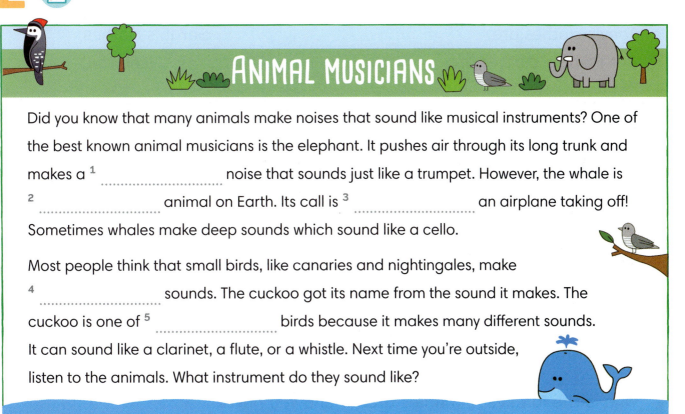

ANIMAL MUSICIANS

Did you know that many animals make noises that sound like musical instruments? One of the best known animal musicians is the elephant. It pushes air through its long trunk and makes a ¹............... noise that sounds just like a trumpet. However, the whale is ²............... animal on Earth. Its call is ³............... an airplane taking off! Sometimes whales make deep sounds which sound like a cello.

Most people think that small birds, like canaries and nightingales, make ⁴............... sounds. The cuckoo got its name from the sound it makes. The cuckoo is one of ⁵............... birds because it makes many different sounds. It can sound like a clarinet, a flute, or a whistle. Next time you're outside, listen to the animals. What instrument do they sound like?

1 louder	loud	the loudest
2 the most loud	the loudest	the louder
3 louder than	more loud than	loudest than
4 most beautiful	the most beautiful	the beautiful
5 more interesting than	interesting	the most interesting

97

3 Look and write. Use the words in parentheses.

1 Sarah is .... Francis,
   but Tony is .... person. (famous)
2 Francis is .... Tony and Sarah.
   In fact, she's .... person there. (short)
3 Tony's clothes are .... Sarah's clothes,
   but Francis' clothes are .... (colorful)

4 Write the words in order. Use the word in bold in the correct form.

1 is / watching live concerts / watching TV / **exciting**

   ....

2 is / place in Greece / the Acropolis / **famous**

   ....

3 is / playing an instrument / listening to music / **difficult**

   ....

5 Read and circle. Then answer for you.

1 Who is **the funniest** / **funnier than** friend you have?

   ....

2 Who is the **more intelligent** / **the most intelligent** person you know?

   ....

3 Which animals are **the scariest** / **scarier than** a shark?

   ....

Writing

1 Read and check (✓) the sentences that get the reader's attention.

1 a It's a good experience. ☐
  b It's the best experience. ☐
2 a Listen to the most amazing traditional music in the world. ☐
  b Listen to amazing traditional music. ☐
3 a Come and watch a famous band. ☐
  b Come and watch the most famous band in the city. ☐

2 Read and make notes about the event you chose.

1 What's the event?
....
2 What day and time is it?
....
3 How much do tickets cost?
....
4 Where is it?
....
5 What can people do there?
....

3 Write an ad for your event. Use your ideas from Activity 2 to help you.

(!) Remember
1 Write a title.
2 Use -est/the most to get the reader's attention.
3 Include all the important information.
4 Write neatly.

99

Now I Know

1 Find and circle the words.

K	K	C	L	A	R	I	N	E	T	T
O	R	C	H	E	S	T	R	A	N	R
C	J	J	F	K	D	K	O	I	K	U
E	J	G	B	S	T	R	I	N	G	M
L	I	S	K	O	X	T	U	N	L	P
L	I	X	G	M	V	G	R	M	R	E
O	T	R	O	M	B	O	N	E	B	T
V	S	A	X	O	P	H	O	N	E	L

2 Read and complete.

> famous   hang out   magazines   modern   musicians

1 I like to _____ with my friends at the park or at the mall.
2 We had a great time listening to our favorite _____ play at the festival.
3 There are a lot of _____ about computers in the library.
4 My city is _____ for its restaurants and museums.
5 The new neighborhood has a lot of _____ buildings.

100

3 Look and write.

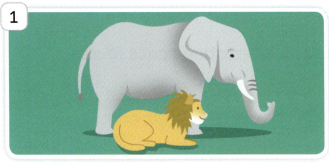

The lion ....

Car 2 ....,
but Car 3 ....

4 Choose four phrases and write sentences about your family and friends.

| bored with | happy with | surprised at | worried about | tired of |

1 ....
2 ....
3 ....
4 ....

Things I learn

1 What are your three favorite words in this unit?

....

2 Write something you think is interesting about:

musical instruments ....
different forms of entertainment ....

3 Which kind of entertainment do you think is the most interesting? Why?

....
....

101

8 Why is space interesting?

1 What do you know about space? Write two interesting space facts.

....

....

2 Circle the words about space. Then think about and write one thing you learn in this unit.

star   rocket   airplane   the Sun   country   car   pilot

....

3 🎬 BBC 8-1 Watch the video. Then look and write.

Earth	Jupiter	Mars
Mercury	Neptune	Saturn
the Sun	Uranus	Venus

1 ....
2 ....
3 ....
4 ....
5 ....
6 ....
7 ....
8 ....
9 ....

4 🎬 BBC 8-1 Read and complete with the names of the planets. Watch the video again to check.

The Sun's diameter is more than 100 times bigger than the diameter of the ¹................... . ² .... is called the red planet. ³ .... and ⁴ .... have rings around them. The farthest planet from the Sun is ⁵ .... and nearest is ⁶ .... The biggest planet in our solar system is ⁷ .... and the smallest is ⁸ ....

102

Vocabulary 1

1 Read and circle.

1 That boy is very **rude** / **bright**. He took my pen without asking.
2 It's very **frightened** / **bright** outside. Put on your sunglasses.
3 John was very **worried** / **cry** when he couldn't find his keys.
4 We're in a **rude** / **hurry**, the concert starts in five minutes!

2 Read and write. Use the words from the box. There's one extra word.

> bright   bump   frightened   moon   rude

1 You get this when you hit your head. ....
2 This is the feeling you get when something scares you. ....
3 This describes someone who isn't polite. ....
4 We can see this in the sky at night. ....

3 Read, look, and complete.

Last night was terrible! An ¹................... woke me up at midnight.

Then I was very ²................... because I heard a strange noise outside.

I woke up my dad and we went into the garden. The ³................... was

very bright, but Dad didn't notice the ⁴................... on the ground. He fell

and hit his head! I was so ⁵................... that I started to

⁶.................... Mom heard me crying and ran outside in a ⁷....................

Dad had a big ⁸................... on his head, but he was OK so we all went

back to bed. I still don't know what the noise was!

103

4 Think and write.

1 Why do people cry?
....

2 What can you see mainly at night?
....

Word study: words to describe feelings

5 Add *-ed* or *-d* to these words to make words that describe feelings. Then check (✓) how you felt today.

> confuse   embarrass   excite   please   scare   shock

1 *embarrassed* ☐
2 .... ☐
3 .... ☐
4 .... ☐
5 .... ☐
6 .... ☐

6 Complete the sentences. Use the words from Activity 5.

1 My baby brother was .... to see snow for the first time.
2 I'm a bit .... about this word. What does it mean?
3 My cheeks always feel hot when I get ....
4 Milo is .... because he scored a goal in the soccer match.
5 My brother is .... of snakes and spiders, but I love them!

7 Read and complete for you.

1 I feel .... when ....
2 I feel .... when ....

104

Reading 1

1 Read the story. Is Sun a good friend? Why?

WHY THE SUN AND THE MOON LIVE IN THE SKY

Long, long ago Moon and her husband, Sun, lived on Earth. Sun had a very good friend, Water. Sun often visited Water's house, but Water didn't visit Sun. Finally, Sun asked Water, "Why don't you visit me?" Water said, "I have a very big family. Your house is too small."

"Don't worry. We don't mind having a full house," said Sun.

"But what if there's no space for you and Moon? I don't want to be rude," said Water.

Sun promised Water to build a very big house. He and Moon worked hard for many weeks. It was very tiring, but they were pleased when the new house was finished. The next day, they invited Water and his family to visit. When Water and his family arrived, Water looked at Sun and Moon's new house. "Are you sure we can come in?" said Water.

"Of course!" said Sun, feeling confident. "Our new house is very big! Come in!"

Water went inside the house with his family. Soon the kitchen and the living room were full. Moon was worried. "Maybe this was a bad idea," she said to Sun.

"Nonsense!" he replied.

As more and more water came into the house, Sun and Moon had to go and sit on the roof. The water started coming out of the windows and onto the roof. There was so much water that Moon and Sun had to move up to the sky.

And that is where they stayed.

2 Read the story again. Write *M* (Moon), *S* (Sun), or *W* (Water).

1 Who doesn't want to be rude? ....
2 Who makes a promise? ....
3 Who works hard? ....
4 Who feels tired? ....
5 Who is confident? ....
6 Who feels worried? ....

3 💡 Is it always good to be confident? Why?/Why not?

....

105

Grammar 1

It's interesting. I'm interested.
It was frightening. They were frightened.
The stars are amazing. He's amazed.
The movie was boring. We were bored.

1 Look, read, and complete with *-ed* or *-ing*.

The rollercoaster was excit_____.
Tyrone was excit_____.

Gemma felt relax_____ when she listened to relax_____ music.

Riding a bike uphill is very tir_____. I'm so tir_____ now.

Dad gave Mom a surpris_____ birthday gift. She was surpris_____ when she opened it.

2 Read and complete.

| interested   interesting | | amazed   amazing |

1 The museum about prehistoric times was really _____.

2 I was _____ to hear that you were born in Australia.

3 My friend was _____ when she won the first prize in the competition.

4 Our vacation in Japan was _____.

106

3 Read and complete using the correct form of each word.

1 James was _____ (surprise) when he passed the difficult test.
2 We were _____ (please) when Joanna told us she was coming to visit.
3 Our neighbor plays loud music all the time. It's very _____ (annoy).
4 It's so _____ (embarrass) when my dad dances at parties.
5 My parents get _____ (worry) if I'm late.

4 Read and complete. Use the correct form of the words from the box.

| amaze | confuse | disappoint | excite | frighten | interest |

1 Tom and Jenny were too _____ to go out in the dark.
2 Dad was very _____ because he got a new job.
3 I found the story _____. There were too many characters in it.
4 The documentary about space was very _____.
5 Sam was _____ at the things he could see with his new telescope.
6 Juan was _____ because he wasn't invited to the party.

5 Write five true sentences about you. Use the words from the box.

| amazing | bored | disappointed | embarrassing | exciting |
| frightened | interesting | surprised | worried |

Vocabulary 2

1 Look and circle.

1	2	3	4	5
rocket	launch	telescope	planet	space station
scientist	float	laboratory	orbit	spacesuit

2 Read and complete the words.

1 The s__ i__ __t__ __ __ explained what he's trying to discover.
2 We watched the rocket l__ __n__ __ into space on TV – it was amazing!
3 It takes 365 days for the Earth to __ r__ __t the Sun.
4 __pa__ __s__ __ __s protect astronauts when they do space walks.

3 Read and complete. Use the words from the box.

| laboratory | launched | orbits | planets | rocket | Space Station |

RICHARD IS AN ASTRONAUT. WE ASKED HIM YOUR QUESTIONS!

How many [1] .... are there in our solar system?
There are eight. In the past, people thought there were nine, but in 2006 scientists decided not to include Pluto.

Where do you live when you go into space?
I live on the International [2] .... It's a very big object which [3] .... the Earth 16 times a day. Astronauts use it as a giant science [4] .... – when we are there, we study lots of different things about space.

When did people first go to the Moon?
In 1969, the U.S.A. [5] .... a [6] .... called Apollo 11, carrying three astronauts. Neil Armstrong and Buzz Aldrin were the first people to walk on the Moon.

4 What do you need to go into space? Draw and write.

Vocabulary challenge: space words

5 Look, read, and match.

1  satellite ☐

2  galaxy ☐

3  black hole ☐

4 constellation ☐

5  comet ☐

a   a very large group of stars and planets
b   an object which orbits the Earth to receive and send information
c   a big ball of ice that moves quickly through space
d   a very dark area in space from which light can't escape
e   a group of stars that make a shape or pattern in the sky

6 Read and complete. Use the words from Activity 5.

1 .... show us what's happening on Earth and in space, and help us communicate.

2 Orion, Scorpius, Lyra, and Hydra are some of the .... we can see in the night sky without a telescope.

3 Halley's .... appears every 76 years and has a bright tail of gas and dust.

4 The Milky Way is the .... we live in. It has billions of stars.

5 A .... is so strong that if something goes inside it, it can never get out.

109

Reading 2

1 Read the text. Add more information to column 3 of the KWL chart. Look again at column 2 of the KWL chart in your Student's Book. Did the text answer all your questions?

Learning to be an ASTRONAUT

Did you know that astronauts sometimes have other jobs first? They can be engineers, science teachers or scientists. Then they have to train to be an astronaut for two years.

The US space programme is in Houston, Texas. There the trainee astronauts study science, Maths, medicine and languages. One important language for working on the International Space Station is Russian because the Control Centre is in Russia. The trainees also practise living without gravity in special machines. They practise in a plane called the Weightless Wonder. The plane goes up and then falls for 20–25 seconds. During this time they experience zero gravity.

The trainees also go underwater in a huge swimming pool to practise walking in space and learn how to move objects in space – objects float away in space just like they do underwater.

Astronauts take public speaking classes because they often have to talk about their work. They learn about the cultures of the other countries that send astronauts to the International Space Station, too!

Astronauts also have survival training in case they land in the wrong place when they go back to Earth and rescuers can't find them.

Learning to be an ASTRONAUT
L = What I **learned**

2 Read the text again and match.

1 Astronauts have to train for
2 The ISS Control Center
3 Being underwater helps astronauts learn
4 They do survival training

a in case they land in a wrong place.
b two years.
c is in Russia.
d how to move in space.

3 For what other jobs do people train for a long time?

....

....

110

Grammar 2

> **Once** means one time and **twice** means two times.
>
> **How often does** the Moon orbit the Earth?
> The Moon orbits the Earth **once a month**.
>
> **How often does** the Earth orbit the Sun?
> The Earth orbits the Sun **once a year**.
>
> **How often do** the astronauts see the sunrise?
> They see the sunrise **every 90 minutes**.

1 Read and circle.

1 How often **do / does** you go to the library?
2 How often **do / does** your parents help you with your homework?
3 How often **do / does** Max wash up?
4 How often **do / does** Josie take her dog for a walk?

2 Read and circle six time phrases. Then write.

I have a very busy schedule. I take my dog for a walk and I feed the cat twice a day. I also have to make my bed every day. I have a lot of hobbies, too. Every Tuesday, I have a piano lesson and twice a month I go to water polo training. Every Wednesday and Thursday, I have chess club and I play in chess tournaments three times a year.

1 once a week
2 every two weeks
3 every 12 hours *twice a day*
4 twice a week
5 every four months
6 once a day

111

3   Listen and check (✓).

1 What does Cody do twice a week?

a  b  c

2 How often do Mary and Lia visit their cousins?

a  b  c

3 Where does Vicky go once a month?

a  b  c

4 Write the questions in order. Then answer for you.

1 often / you / how / do / go / the / movie theater / to

....?

....

2 your / parents / often / go / how / shopping / do

....?

....

3 give / often / how / does / your / teacher / a test / you

....?

....

4 do / play / you / often / how / video games

....?

....

Writing

1 Read these two email extracts. Which one shows that the writer is interested in the astronaut's life?

a

Hi Mariel,

Thanks for your last email. I love reading about space, too! I watch a lot of documentaries about space on TV.

I want to be an astronaut one day and work on the International Space Station. What do you want to be?

Write back soon,

Ellie

b

Hello Yuri ,

I love learning about space. Can you tell me what it feels like to be in space? What does the Earth look like from space? Can you see the other planets in our solar system? What do you do when you work at the International Space Station?

Best wishes,

Ryan

2 Circle the things you would like to ask an astronaut. Then write two more.

where he/she sleeps   what he/she eats   how old he/she is

what he/she likes about space   what his/her favorite planet is

3 Write an email to an astronaut. Use your ideas from Activity 2 to help you.

(!) Remember

1 Greet the person you're writing to.
2 Ask questions to show you're interested.
3 Use paragraphs.
4 Say goodbye and write your name at the end.

113

Now I Know

1 Read and circle.

1 Ruby is **bored / boring** because the book she's reading isn't **excited / exciting**.
2 Mustafa and Pete were **worrying / worried** about missing the **interesting / interested** show.
3 The movie was **fascinating / fascinated** at first, but I got **tired / tiring** watching it because it was too long.
4 The loud noise was **frightened / frightening** and it made the baby cry.
5 We felt **disappointed / disappointing** because we didn't do well in the test.

2 Read and circle T (true) or F (false).

1 Some people cry when they have a bump on the head.   T   F
2 The moon orbits the Sun.   T   F
3 People are in a hurry because they have a lot of time.   T   F
4 Owls have big eyes because it's bright at night.   T   F
5 There are a lot of sticks in the forest.   T   F
6 Parents are worried when children are late.   T   F

3 Read and write the letters in order.

When an astronaut goes outside her **ckorte** [1] ...., she needs to wear a **cespatuis** [2] ....

When a **iencsttsi** [3] .... wants to study things in space, they use a very powerful **scpeoltee** [4] ....

A **scepa itastno** [5] .... is like a very big **orarybtola** [6] .... which **otasfl** [7] .... in space.

114

4 Read the answers. Then write the questions.

1 _____?
I have tennis lessons three times a week.

2 _____?
He goes to the movie theater once a month.

3 _____?
Alice goes swimming twice a week.

4 _____?
They go camping once a year.

5 Write true sentences about you. Use the time phrases from the box.

| every day | once a week | three times a year | twice a week |

Things I learn

1 What are your three favorite words in this unit?

_____

2 Write something you think is interesting about:

space stations _____
astronaut training _____

3 Why is it important to study space?

_____

115

9 How are homes different?

1 What makes your home special? What's the most important thing in your home? Why?

....

....

2 Circle the words that describe your home. Then think about and write one thing you learn in this unit.

> beautiful   boring   cold   interesting
> new   old   relaxing   ugly   warm

....

3   Watch the video. Then look and write.

> cloth   ladder   stilts   straw

....

4 Complete the sentences using words from Activity 3. Watch the video again to check.

1 You have to go up a .... to get to the tree house.
2 The home in the Sahara Desert is made of .... so they can put their home wherever they want.
3 The house in the ocean has .... to keep it dry from the sea.
4 The mud house in India has a roof made of ....

116

Vocabulary 1

1 Find and write the words. Then look and match.

A	B	C	D	E	F	G	H	I	J	K	L	M	N	O	P	Q	R	S	T	U	V	W	X	Y	Z
1	2	3	4	5	6	7	8	9	10	11	12	13	14	15	16	17	18	19	20	21	22	23	24	25	26

a ___ ___ ___ ___ ___
   1 20 20 9 3

b ___ ___ ___ ___
   18 15 15 6

c ___ ___ ___ ___ ___
   19 20 15 14 5

d ___ ___ ___ ___
   23 15 15 4

e ___ ___ ___ ___ ___ ___ ___
   2 1 12 3 15 14 25

f ___ ___ ___ ___ ___
   19 20 5 5 16

2 Read and complete. Then match.

| balcony | build | flat | roof | stone | sweep | view |

1 The bike ride wasn't difficult.
2 Mom likes to sit on the _____
3 Some old houses in my village are
4 People sometimes cut down trees
5 We climbed to the top of
6 The _____
7 It's my chore to _____

a made of _____ .
b tower to see the _____ .
c the leaves in the fall.
d The road was _____ .
e in the morning and drink tea.
f to _____ houses.
g protects a house from rain.

117

3 Draw and write about your home. Use words from Activities 1 and 2.

This is a picture of my home. It's made of
....
It has .... ,
.... , ... ,
and ....

Vocabulary challenge: kinds of homes

4 Look and write.

hut   igloo   motor home   stilt house

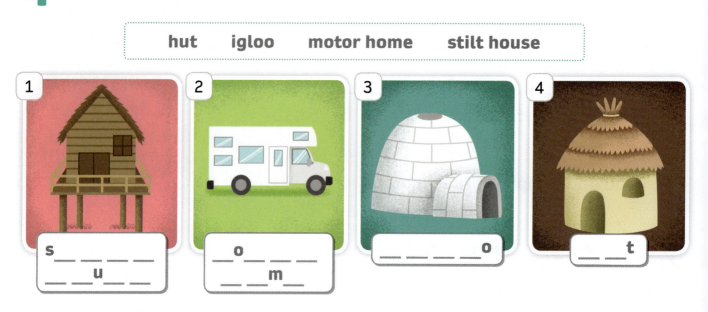

1 s _ _ _ _
   _ _ u _ _

2 _ o _ _ _
   _ _ m _ _

3 _ _ _ _ _ o _

4 _ _ _ t

5 Read and complete. Use the words from Activity 4.

1 I want to buy a .... so I can travel to many different places.
2 Some Inuit people build an .... from snow to sleep in when they go hunting for food.
3 If you live in a .... you have to use a boat to travel around.
4 Dad built a .... made of wood for us to play in.

118

Reading 1

1 Read the story and underline the most important information.

MRS MOUSE AND HER HOUSE

Mrs Mouse lived with her children in a little house in the country. It was made of stone, with a roof made of wood, and there were lots of flowers in the front garden. It was very pretty.

But the children grew and grew. When the family had dinner, two of the children had to sit on the cupboards because there wasn't space at the table. When they went to sleep, one little mouse had to sleep under the bed on the floor. "Mum, we need a bigger house," they said. "We can build a bigger kitchen. We can also make the attic into a bedroom. There's a great view from up there!" said Mrs Mouse. "Would you like to help me find some stones and wood?"
"Yes!" the children said happily.

They went to the forest. It was very dirty. "Look at all this rubbish!" said Mrs Mouse sadly.
"Let's use the rubbish for building."
"What a great idea!" said Mrs Mouse. They took the rubbish home. The older children used old wooden boxes to build a new kitchen with a big table. They used glass bottles to make windows and plastic bags for the roof. The younger children swept the attic, while Mrs Mouse made a bed from a cardboard box.

Soon the house was ready. Everyone sat together at the table for dinner. At bedtime, the older children slept in the attic and the littlest mouse slept in a bed downstairs. Everyone was very happy.

2 Use the information you underlined in Activity 1 to write a summary in your notebook.

3 Think and write.

1 The mice reuse the trash from the forest. Why is this good for the environment?

....

2 Are any parts of your home made from recycled materials?

....

Grammar 1

Would you like to visit Hong Kong?
Yes, I would like to visit Hong Kong.
No, I wouldn't like to visit Hong Kong.

Would he like to meet an alien?
Yes, he'd like to meet an alien.
No, he wouldn't like to meet an alien.

1 Read and match.

1 I'd like
2 He would like to
3 She'd like to have
4 They

a would like to see the new movie.
b visit China one day.
c a pizza and a salad, please.
d lunch by the ocean.

2 Write the questions in order. Then look and write the answers.

1 where / go / he / would / to / like
   ....?
   ....

2 like / she / to / would / do / what
   ....?
   ....

3 to / city / which / visit / they / like / would
   ....?
   ....

4 meet / would / like / she / to / who
   ....?
   ....

People
Dua's roof
the Doctor's name

There was a lot of snow on Brad's roof.
The floor of the attic is dirty!

Things
the roof of the house
the name of the spaceship

3 Read and circle.

1 There's a great view from the **30th floor of the tower / tower's 30th floor**.
2 **Joe's red kite / The red kite of Joe** is new.
3 **The house of my grandma / My grandma's house** is old.
4 Be careful! The **knife's blade / blade of the knife** is sharp.
5 There was a steep path to get to the **top of the mountain / mountain's top**.

4 Look and write sentences.

1

Alice / dog / small

3

table / leg / broken

2

woman / flowers / colorful

4

clock / cogs / not stone

121

Vocabulary 2

1 Write the letters in order. Then label the pictures with five of the words.

1 r a i s t s ....
2 s k c r i b ....
3 r r w o n a ....
4 c c r n o t e e ....
5 n e t m s e a b ....
6 m e o v ....
7 l e e t a v r o ....
8 l a e m t ....
9 s t c i l a p ....
10 d e i w ....

a

b

c

d

e

....

2 Read and match.

1 This takes you up and down inside a tall building.
2 It's a room under a house that has no windows.
3 When you change from one home to another.
4 We use these to build walls and houses.
5 A strong material that we use to make cans, jewelry, and cars.

a move
b metal
c bricks
d elevator
e basement

3 Read and cross out the wrong word.

1 The doors in the old museum are **narrow** / **wide** / **plastic**.
2 We use **concrete** / **stairs** / **elevators** to go up and down a building.
3 We use **bricks** / **basements** / **concrete** to build houses.
4 We can recycle **metal** / **plastic** / **stairs**.
5 **Basements** / **Metals** / **Stairs** are part of a house.

4 Read and complete. Then write sentences with the words you didn't use.

> concrete   elevator   metal   move   narrow   plastic   stairs

1 The burglar couldn't get through the window because it was very ....
2 I walked up the .... because the .... was broken.
3 Put all things made of .... and .... in the recycling bins.
4 ....
5 ....

Word study: words with *st*, *br*, *pl*

5 Read and circle the words with *st*, *br*, and *pl*.

1 My house had a red brick wall.
2 We should recycle plastic if we want to help the environment.
3 The town has narrow stone streets.
4 My city has many interesting places to visit.
5 Turn left at the end of the road and cross the bridge.
6 I love watching planes take off and land at airports.

6 Match to make as many words as you can. Then write the words.

st	ate	uto	anet	ar
br	airs	oom	ory	ead
pl	own	ore	other	ant

....
....
....

123

Reading 2

1 Read the text. Then complete the sentences.

HOMES AROUND THE WORLD

COOBER PEDY
AUSTRALIA

This Australian town is famous for its underground homes. More than 1,500 families live underground, and some of the homes are 60 years old or more. When people want a bigger bedroom, they just dig out the rock. They stop when the room is the right size.

DIETIKON
SWITZERLAND

There are nine underground homes around a small lake in this town in Switzerland. The homes have an interesting, modern design, but they aren't easy to build. First, you have to make the shape of the rooms with metal. Next, you put concrete on the metal. Then you put earth and grass on the top.

LESOTHO
SOUTHERN AFRICA

Lesotho in southern Africa has small, round houses called rondavels. They're traditional homes and easy to build. All the materials are natural. People make the walls with stone and mud, and then they make the floors with cow dung. They have roofs made of wood and straw. Today, rondavels are mainly used by tourists.

NUNAVUT
NORTHERN CANADA

Igloos are round and small, but very strong. They're completely made of snow, cut into blocks. They have a small door and small holes in the walls, so the fresh air can come in. People who visit northern Canada on vacation can build their own igloo to sleep in!

1 The homes in Coober Pedy and Dietikon are similar because ....
   They're different because ....

2 The homes in Lesotho and Nunavut are similar because ....
   They're different because ....

2 Do you think it's important for people to build homes that respect their environment?

124

Grammar 2

1st	first	8th	eighth	20th	twentieth
2nd	second	9th	ninth	21st	twenty-first
3rd	third	10th	tenth	22nd	twenty-second
4th	fourth	11th	eleventh	23rd	twenty-third
5th	fifth	12th	twelfth	24th	twenty-fourth
6th	sixth	13th	thirteenth	30th	thirtieth
7th	seventh	14th	fourteenth		

1 Read and match.

3rd   fifth   9th   twelfth   13th   twentieth   24th

ninth   thirteenth   12th   third   5th   twenty-fourth   20th

2 Read and write the day of the week.

1 the seventh day ....
2 the twenty-third day ....
3 the first day ....
4 the thirteenth day ....
5 the twenty-fifth day ....
6 the thirtieth day ....

January

Sunday		5	12	19	26
Monday		6	13	20	27
Tuesday		7	14	21	28
Wednesday	1	8	15	22	29
Thursday	2	9	16	23	30
Friday	3	10	17	24	31
Saturday	4	11	18	25	

3 Look and complete.

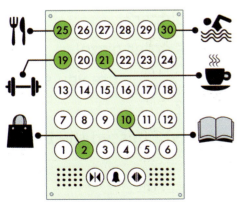

1 The restaurant is on the _twenty-fifth_ floor.
2 The gym is on the .... floor.
3 The store is on the .... floor.
4 The café is on the .... floor.
5 The swimming pool is on the .... floor.
6 The library is on the .... floor.

125

> **Wh- questions**
>
> **when** – a time   **When did** Ahmed move to Shibam?
> **where** – a place   **Where does** your uncle live?
> **who** – a person   **Who do** you live with?
> **what** – a thing   **What are** the walls made of?
> **why** – a reason   **Why were** tall buildings safer?
> **which** – a choice **Which** subjects **do** you study at school?

4 Read and choose.

1 **Jayden:** What floor is your bedroom on?
  Tom: a It's number one. b It's next to my sister's room.
  c It's on the second floor.

2 **Hazel:** Where's your apartment?
  Nick: a It's on the first floor. b It's on one floor. c It's on one.

3 **Juana:** When is your birthday?
  Max: a On January five. b On January fifth.
  c On January fifteen.

4 **Asher:** Who lives on Seventh Street?
  Dina: a Tim's house. b Tim's family. c It's Tim.

5 **Veronica:** Why did you move?
  Gabriel: a We moved last year. b My dad got a new job.
  c Yes, I did.

5 Read and complete.

1 **Ahmed:** _Where_ 's the park?
  Ellen: The park is on Third Street.

2 **Rafael:** _____ 's this?
  Elliot: It's Janet, my sister.

3 **Dad:** _____ do you finish school?
  Astrid: Around two o'clock.

4 **Millie:** _____ would you like for dinner?
  Jeff: Let's order pizza!

5 **Mom:** _____ are you so late?
  Alfredo: Sorry! I missed the bus.

Writing

1 Read these paragraphs from two different blogs. Which one is better? Why?

MY PERFECT HOME

a

My perfect home is a small hut on the beach. It's made of wood. I'd like to have a bedroom, a kitchen, and a bathroom. The kitchen can be smalla. I'd like to eat outside and watch the ocean.

b

My perfect home is a stone house in the mountains. It has three bedrooms and two bathrooms. I'd like to have a big living room and a nice kitchen, too. I'd also like to have a balcony with a view of the mountains.

2 Read and make notes about your perfect home.

1 Where is it?

2 What's it made of?

3 What rooms does it have?

4 What would you like to do in it?

3 Write a blog post about your perfect home. Use your ideas from Activity 2 to help you.

(!) Remember
1 Write a title.
2 Use paragraphs.
3 Use *too* and *also*.
4 Use describing words.

127

Now I Know

1 Complete the crossword. What's the hidden word?

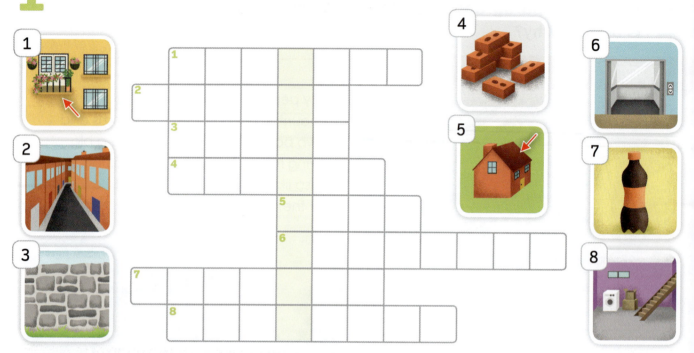

2 Read and circle.

1 I love sitting on my **balcony** / **attic** in the summer and reading a book.
2 There was a beautiful **view** / **wood** of the ocean from our hotel room.
3 I couldn't ride my bike up the **flat** / **steep** street.
4 We used **plastic** / **stone** cups and plates at my party.
5 I don't like **stairs** / **elevators**, so I never go in them.

3 Read, think, and write.

1 Write five materials.

....

2 Write two things that we use to go up or down a building.

....

3 Write two words to describe a street or river.

....

4 Write two words to describe land.

....

4 Look and write *st*, *rd*, *nd*, or *th*. Then write the number.

1 1 __st__ __first__
2 11 _____
3 22 _____
4 29 _____

5 Complete the questions. Use *would like* and the words from the box. Then answer for you.

> be   live   ~~try~~   visit

1 Which new food _would you like to try_ ?
   I'd like to try _____ .

2 Where _____ when you're a grown-up?
   _____

3 What _____ when you're older?
   _____

4 Who _____ next week?
   _____

Things I learn

1 What are your three favorite words in this unit?

_____

2 Write something you think is interesting about:

homes around the world: _____
parts of homes: _____

3 Why do people in different countries build different kinds of homes? Why do they use different materials?

_____

129

10 How do we take care of our body?

1 Why is it important to take care of our bodies? Write the names of two body parts and say why we need them.

....

....

2 Circle things that are good for our bodies. Then think about and write one thing you learn in this unit.

drinking water   eating junk food   eating fruit   watching TV

....

3 🔘 BBC 10-1 Watch the video. Then look and write.

> GP (general practitioner)   patient   stethoscope
> take blood pressure

....

4 🔘 BBC 10-1 Read the tips and circle **T** (true) or **F** (false). Watch the video again to check.

Dr Natalie Crowe's Top Tips:

- Don't talk to people and make them feel at ease.   **T   F**
- Think about the person as a whole and their everyday life.   **T   F**
- You have to be able to work slowly.   **T   F**

130

Vocabulary 1

1 Find 10 words and label the pictures.

neckstomachfeverbandagerestsickpaletakemedicinebackshoulder

1 ....

3 ....

5 ....

7 ....

9 ....

2 ....

4 ....

6 ....

8 ....

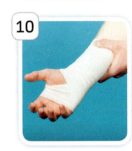
10 ....

2 Read and match.

1 You have this when you're sick. Your body is hot.   a rest
2 You do this when you feel tired or sick.   b bandage
3 The food you eat goes there.   c fever
4 If you hurt your arm or leg, you put this around it.   d stomach

3 Read and complete. Use the words from the box.

| back | pale | shoulder | take medicine |

1 We shouldn't _____ without asking a doctor first.
2 The baby put his head on my _____ and fell asleep.
3 I hurt my _____ lifting those heavy boxes.
4 I knew Anne was sick because she was very _____.

131

4 When was the last time you were sick? What happened?

....

....

Vocabulary challenge: injuries

5 Look and write. Use the words from the box.

break   bruise   burn   cut   sprain

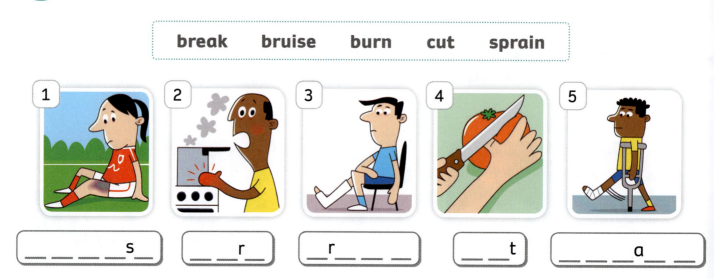

1. _ _ _ _ s _ _
2. _ _ r _ _
3. _ r _ _ _
4. _ _ t
5. _ _ _ a _ _

6 Read and circle.

Subject: Your birthday party

Dear Alexis,
I'm sorry, but I can't come to your birthday party. I had a horrible week.
On Monday, I made a salad and ¹ **burned / cut** my finger. On Tuesday, I made some tea and the cup fell on the floor. Luckily, I didn't ² **sprain / burn** myself!
Yesterday, I fell down the stairs. I have a few blue and black ³ **sprains / bruises**. I'm lucky I didn't ⁴ **burn / break** my leg, but I ⁵ **sprained / cut** my ankle. I'm not allowed in the kitchen anymore and I have to rest.
I hope your party is great. Send me pictures!
Love,
Selen

132

Reading 1

1 Read the story. Why did Fran feel tired?

FRAN AND THE ALIENS

"Yes!" said Fran. "I won again!"
Alien Attack was her favorite video game, and she played it for hours every day. She was very good at it.

She started the game again. But before it finished, her father came into her bedroom, and she made a silly mistake. She sighed.
"Your dinner is ready," he said. "Come downstairs and eat."
Fran didn't feel hungry, and she didn't want to stop her game. "Not now, Dad. Maybe later."
"Fran, you need to eat," her father said.
Fran went downstairs, but she only ate a little. She couldn't stop thinking about how to beat the Alien Master.
"You look tired. You should go straight to bed," said Fran's mother.
"Yes, Mom," said Fran, but she went back to her computer. By 2 a.m., she was on Level 89.

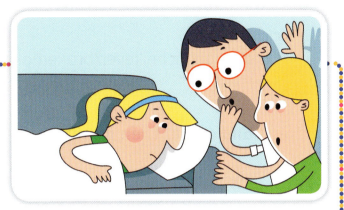

"Maybe I can get to Level 100!" she said, and continued playing.

The next day, Fran couldn't focus in class. The teacher called Fran's parents and they took her home.
"What's wrong, Fran? Why are you so tired? You don't have a fever."
"I didn't go to bed last night," said Fran quietly. "I stayed up playing *Alien Attack*."
Fran's parents were shocked.
"Your body needs to rest, Fran, just like it needs food and exercise," said her dad.
From that day on, Fran ate healthy food, went to bed early, and did exercise every day. She felt much happier and healthier. She still played video games, but not as much as before.

2 Read the story again. Then read and check (✓) the correct sentences.

1 Fran felt hungry at dinnertime. ☐
2 Fran couldn't focus at school. ☐
3 Fran's parents were surprised that Fran didn't go to bed. ☐

3 💡 Why is it important to be honest with your parents?

....

133

Grammar 1

> **What's** the matter? **What's** wrong?
> **I'm** sick/fine.
> **I have** a stomachache/fever/broken arm.
> My leg **hurts**.

1 Read and circle. Then match.

1 **Fin:** What's wrong, Carlos?
   Carlos: I **break** / **broke** my leg at soccer practice yesterday.

2 **Sarah:** What's the matter, Raven?
   Raven: I **have** / **has** a fever.

3 **May:** What's wrong, Paul?
   Paul: Oh, I **have** / **had** a bad headache.

4 **Evrim:** What's the matter, Dad?
   Dad: I **hurts** / **hurt** my shoulder playing tennis.

 a
 b
 c
 d

2 Write the words in order.

1 matter / the / what's

   ....?

2 has / he / a / stomachache

   ....

3 I / a / arm / broken / have

   ....

4 the / has / Emily / to / to / go / doctor

   ....

5 to / they / rest / have

   ....

I have a stomachache. **I have to** drink lots of water.
He has a broken arm. **He has to** have an X-ray.
She has a fever. **She has to** drink water and take some medicine.

3 What's the matter with each person? Listen and match.
05

1 Zahra ☐   2 Jason ☐   3 Mom ☐   4 Dominic ☐   5 Holly ☐

a   b   c   d   e   f

4 Read and write.

1 fever / medicine
Sonia _____ .

2 broken leg / X-ray
Alp _____ .

5 What do they have to do? Write.

1 Antonio has a broken arm. He *has to go to the doctor* _____ .
2 Jen has a sprained leg. She _____ .
3 Dad and Emma are sick. _____
4 Deniz has a stomachache. _____
5 Betty has a headache. _____

Vocabulary 2

1 Read and cross out the wrong word.

1 A healthy diet helps the **brain / cold / heart** work well.
2 I'm allergic to flowers and always **save your life / cough / sneeze** when I'm close to them.
3 Your **brain / skin / heart** is inside your body.
4 Doing exercise is good for our **heart / muscles / sneezes**.

2 Find and circle eight words. Then read and write.

G	H	E	A	V	A	B	H	E	C	N	S
T	E	C	O	L	D	R	G	N	C	S	N
V	A	C	C	I	N	A	T	I	O	N	E
B	R	U	L	S	K	I	N	D	U	E	E
R	T	R	O	N	L	N	E	E	G	E	Z
H	E	S	P	R	E	A	D	B	H	V	E

1 We do these two things when we have a cold. ....
2 This protects us from serious diseases. ....
3 Germs do this and then people get sick. ....
4 This covers your muscles and your body. ....
5 Without these two things, your body can't work. ....
6 You can catch this in winter. ....

3 Look and write.

1

3

5

2

4

6

4 Why are vaccinations important?

....
....

Word study: actions and things

5 Read. Is the word *cough* an action or a thing?

1 Scott is coughing a lot today because he has a bad cold. ....
2 Scott's cough is very bad because he has a bad cold. ....

6 Read and write *A* (action) or *T* (thing).

1 a I have a cut on my finger. ....   b I cut my finger. ....
2 a Can you bandage my ankle? ....   b Can you put a bandage on my ankle? ....
3 a Your sneeze was very loud. ....   b You sneeze very loudly. ....

137

Reading 2

1 Read the leaflet. Look at the underlined words. Read and match.

Why is exercise good?

Exercise isn't only good for your body; it can improve your friendships too. Doing sport with your friends and family makes you more <u>sociable</u>. It's also a great way to meet people and make new friends.

Exercise can make you a happier person too. When you exercise, your body makes chemicals called endorphins. Because of these endorphins, your body doesn't hurt very much when you exercise. And the endorphins also make you feel happy.

Aerobic exercise, like running, cycling and swimming, makes your brain produce serotonin. People who are <u>depressed</u> have low levels of serotonin. More serotonin can help you stop feeling <u>depressed</u> and makes you happy too.

Exercise also helps you become a better student. Scientists found that active students did better at school. When you exercise, chemicals go to the brain and help it grow and develop.

Exercise also helps you become more <u>flexible</u>. You can bend, jump and do all sorts of movements without hurting your body. The more <u>flexible</u> you are, the better your body moves and the stronger your muscles are.

Of course, exercise isn't the only thing that helps us stay happy and healthy. Eating the right food is very important too.

1 A **sociable** person   a can bend and move their body very well.
2 A **flexible** person   b feels very sad for long periods of time.
3 A **depressed** person   c enjoys being with other people.

2 Read the leaflet again. Circle **T** (true) or **F** (false).

1 It's important to only do exercise with friends.   T   F
2 Excercise can help you be healthy.   T   F
3 Aerobic exercise makes you depressed.   T   F

3 💡 What kind of exercise do you do? How does it help your body?

Grammar 2

1 Read and complete with *should* or *shouldn't*.

1 We .... cut down trees because animals lose their homes.
2 We .... recycle paper, plastic, and glass.
3 You .... go to school when you're sick.
4 .... children play video games all day? No, they ....

> You **should** go.
> Jack **shouldn't** come with us.
> **What should** we do?
> We **should** help them.
> **Should** we look for the medicine?
> Yes, we **should**.
> No, we **shouldn't**.

2 Write the words in order. Then circle T (true) or F (false).

1 should / watch TV / children / all day

.... T F

2 should / we / take care / animals / of

.... T F

3 shouldn't / more / trees / plant / people

.... T F

4 always / help / should / we / friends and family / our

.... T F

3 Look and write sentences using *should* or *shouldn't*.

1
2
3
4

1 ....
2 ....
3 ....
4 ....

139

Person	Thing
Someone should get the medicine.	I can't do **everything**.
Everyone was sick.	We should do **something**.

4 Read and choose.

1 There's **someone** / **something** on your back. It's a spider!
2 I put **everything** / **everyone** away and my bedroom is neat now.
3 **Everyone** / **Everything** at the party was happy.
4 **Something** / **Someone** sent me a message, but I don't know who it was.

5 Read and complete with *someone*, *something*, *everyone*, or *everything*.

1 Can I have _____ to eat? I'm hungry!
2 _____ was faster than me. I was the slowest person in the race.
3 _____ didn't put the milk back in the fridge. Who was it?
4 I don't have any homework today because I did _____ yesterday.

6 Look and write sentences using *someone*, *something*, *everyone*, or *everything*.

....

....

....

....

140

Writing

1 Read the two emails. Check (✓) the one that Cathy sent to a person she knows well.

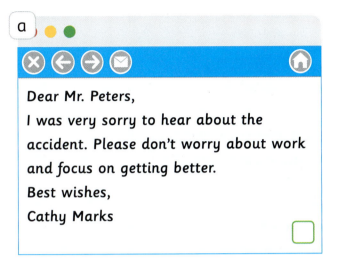

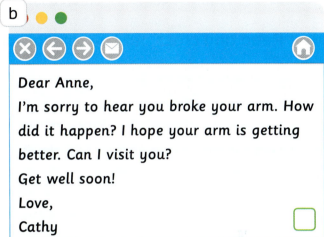

a
Dear Mr. Peters,
I was very sorry to hear about the accident. Please don't worry about work and focus on getting better.
Best wishes,
Cathy Marks

b
Dear Anne,
I'm sorry to hear you broke your arm. How did it happen? I hope your arm is getting better. Can I visit you?
Get well soon!
Love,
Cathy

2 Imagine your friend is sick in the hospital. Answer the questions.

1 Why is your friend in the hospital? What did the doctor say?
....

2 Can you visit them? If not, why?
....

3 What advice do you give your friend?
....

4 What do you wish your friend?
....

3 Write a letter or an email to your friend. Use your ideas from Activity 2 to help you.

(!) Remember
1 Write an appropriate beginning and ending.
2 Use paragraphs.
3 Use time phrases.
4 Write neatly.

141

Now I Know

1 Circle parts of the body.

neck   stomach   shoulder   sneeze   cough   skin   back

cold   vaccination   heart   pale   muscles   bandage   brain

2 Read and cross out the wrong word.

1 John is taking medicine because he **feels sick / is pale / has a fever**.
2 I can't stop **sneezing / coughing / resting**. I think I have a cold!
3 I can't play tennis today. My **stomach / brain / neck** aches.
4 The doctor gave me some cream to put on my **back / shoulder / fever**.
5 A doctor's office usually has **muscles / bandages / vaccinations**.

3 Read and complete. Use the words from the box. There's one extra word.

pale   save your life   sick   spread   take medicine   vaccinations

1 You should cover your nose and mouth when you sneeze, so you don't _____ germs.
2 I knew Joe was sick because he looked very _____.
3 We should respect firefighters because they can _____.
4 _____ hurt, but we have to have them because they protect us.
5 We shouldn't _____ too often – only when we're really sick.

4 Read and complete with *everyone, everything, someone,* or *something*. Then match.

1 There's _____ in the box.
2 _____ is calling. Can you answer?
3 Where's _____ ?
4 The dog ate _____ !

142

5 Complete the questions. Then write the answers.

1 **Mom:** You don't look so good. What's ....?
  Helena: ....

2 **Kim:** What's the ....? You look pale.
  Haru: ....

6 Think about what you learned in this unit.
Write what you should and shouldn't do to keep healthy.

✓
You should

✗
You shouldn't

Things I learn

1 What are your three favorite words in this unit?

....

2 Write something you think is interesting about:

your body ....

germs ....

3 What should you do to take better care of your body?

....

....

143

11 Why is Antarctica special?

1 What parts of the world do you know? What is special about where you live?

....

....

2 Circle the words associated with Antarctica. Then think about and write one thing you learn in this unit.

animals   cars   clean   cold   hot   people   rain   snow

....

3 Watch the video. Then look and write.

cracks   ice sheet   killer whales

....

4 Read and match. Watch the video again to check.

1 The Antarctic ice sheet is
2 Antarctica is one and a half times
3 The ice is up to three
4 75 percent of the Earth's fresh water
5 Killer whales are dangerous because

a miles thick.
b they work in teams.
c the biggest in the world.
d the size of Australia.
e is ice in the Antarctic ice sheet.

144

Vocabulary 1

1 Find and write the words. Then complete the sentences. There's one extra word.

A	B	C	D	E	F	G	H	I	J	K	L	M	N	O	P	Q	R	S	T	U	V	W	X	Y	Z
1	2	3	4	5	6	7	8	9	10	11	12	13	14	15	16	17	18	19	20	21	22	23	24	25	26

a ___ ___ ___ ___ ___ ___ ___
  4   5   7 18   5   5 19

b ___ ___ ___ ___
  4   5   5 16

c ___ ___ ___ ___ ___ ___ ___
 16   5 14   7 21   9 14 19

d ___ ___ ___ ___ ___ ___ ___ ___ ___
 19 15 21 20   8   16 15 12   5

e ___ ___ ___ ___ ___ ___ ___
  6 18   5   5 26   9 14 7

f ___ ___ ___ ___ ___ ___ ___ ___ ___ ___
 20   5 13 16   5 18   1 20 21 18   5

1 It was .... outside, so we stayed indoors.
2 I don't swim in .... water because I'm too afraid.
3 .... are big birds but they can't fly.
4 We didn't enjoy our vacation because it was too hot – 45 .... !
5 The .... is as far south as you can go on Earth.

2 Read and complete. Use the words from the box.

> continent   deep   degrees   freezing
> ice   penguins   temperature

FACT FILE: Antarctica

- Antarctica is the world's fifth largest [1] ....
- Polar bears don't live here, but there are more than six different species of [2] .... They can live for 20 years.
- There's an enormous sheet of [3] .... across Antarctica. It's very [4] .... : in some places up to four kilometers.
- It's the coldest place on Earth. In 1983, the [5] .... dropped here to -89.2 [6] ....
- Antarctica is [7] .... cold but it's a desert, because it doesn't rain here often.

145

3 Write the letters in order. Then choose three words and write sentences.

1 c c k r a ....
2 e x n p o e d i t i ....
3 t n n e t i n o c ....
4 e e e s d g r ....
5 c e i ....
6 n f e i g r e z ....

Word study: synonyms

4 Read and circle the synonyms for the word in bold.

We had to stop the expedition because of the **freezing** weather.

a icy   b wintry   c warm

5 Read and match the synonyms.

1 crack   a pretty
2 expedition   b start
3 beautiful   c hole
4 begin   d organized
5 neat   e trip

6 Write a synonym for each word. Then write a sentence that can use either word.

1 scared / ....

2 big / ....

3 good / ....

4 bad / ....

146

Reading 1

1 Read the journal. Think about the questions in Activity 2 as you read.

MY ANTARCTIC EXPERIENCE

Today is the start of my second week working on the Antarctic Meteorite Programme. The team all come from different countries, but we love working together.

Yesterday was an exciting day. We got ready to go look for space rocks, as we do every morning. We have to put on special clothes, but not too many. We walk a lot when we are looking for meteorites, and we get hot. But we have to be careful not to sweat. In the freezing temperatures of Antarctica, it can be very dangerous to have wet clothes. It's because your body loses heat much more quickly when your clothes are wet.

We travelled on our snowmobiles to an area where there's lots of ice. It's easier to find meteorites on the ice because they're black and we can see them from far away. They're also in very good condition because they don't change in the cold weather.

As we got closer to the ice, I noticed a black spot in the distance. I couldn't believe it – my first meteorite! I picked it up and put it inside a special plastic bag so we can take it home and study it. Meteorites come from asteroids, the Moon or even Mars. They give us lots of information about the materials in our solar system. Some meteorites are millions of years old, so we can learn about the creation of our solar system.

2 Answer the questions. Read the journal again and check.

1 Why is it easy to find meteorites on the ice?

....

2 Why are the meteorites in good condition?

....

3 What can we learn from studying meteorites?

....

3 💡 Imagine you're a scientist. What would you like to study? Why?

....
....

147

Grammar 1

Things we can count with numbers: There can be one or more than one of them.
There are a lot of **skiers**. **There aren't** any **scientists**.
Are there any **penguins** in Antarctica? Yes, **there are**.

Things we can't count with numbers: There can't be more than one of them.
milk (a bottle of milk)   **snow** (three buckets of snow)
land (a piece of land)   **chocolate** (two bars of chocolate)
There's a lot of **snow**. **There isn't** any **oil**.
Is there any **sunlight**? No, **there isn't**.
We use *there is* (or *there's*) for things we can't count.
We use *there are* for more than one thing we can count.

1 Read and circle.

1 **There isn't / There aren't** any ice in the glass.
2 **Is there / Are there** any books in the box?
3 **There is / There are** three pieces of bread on the table.
4 **Is there / Are there** any honey in the jar?
5 **There isn't / There aren't** any children at the park.

2 Look and complete with *There's/isn't* or *There are/aren't*.

1 .... six bottles of orange juice.
2 .... any apples.
3 .... any milk.
4 .... a few jars of honey.
5 .... some chocolate.
6 .... some cereal.

148

3 Look and complete. Use the correct form of *to be* and a word from the box.

> birds   cookies   money   ~~sand~~   soap   water

1. There's a lot of sand at the beach.
2. _____ some _____ in the bottle.
3. _____ any _____ in the bottle? Yes, there _____ .
4. _____ three _____ .
5. _____ any _____ ? No, there _____ .
6. _____ a lot of _____ .

4 Look and write sentences.

1. (traffic) _____
2. (people) _____
3. (dogs) _____
4. (rain) _____

149

Vocabulary 2

1 Read and circle. Then match.

1 Animals in Africa **hunt / layer / migrate** to find grass and water.
2 Don't eat this! It's **waterproof / octopus / poisonous**!
3 People hunt lions and tigers for their **fur / feathers / wings**.
4 Luckily, my coat was **poisonous / waterproof / layer** and I didn't get wet.
5 My birthday cake was very big. It had six **layers / feathers / octopus**.
6 Whales can eat 40 million **fur / krill / wings** a day!

a b c d e f

2 Read and match.

1 fur   a a sea animal with eight arms
2 wing   b these cover birds' bodies
3 feathers   c the hair which covers animals' bodies
4 hunt   d the body part a bird or insect uses to fly
5 octopus   e kill an animal for food or for a part of its body

3 Circle the odd one out. Then write sentences using the words you circled.

1 waterproof   octopus   poisonous
2 krill   feather   wing
3 hunt   poisonous   migrate
4 feather   krill   octopus

....
....
....
....

Vocabulary challenge: animal body parts

4 Look, read, and complete.

hump

antlers

mane

whiskers

hooves

tentacles

1 .... are horns that grow on some animals' heads.
2 Some sea creatures have .... They use them for moving and holding things.
3 .... is the long hair on an animal's neck or around its face.
4 Some animals keep water in a .... on their back.
5 Animals like horses and cows don't have feet. They have ....
6 Cats' .... help them walk in the dark.

5 Write the headings using words from Activity 4. Then add one more animal at the bottom of each column.

1	2	hooves	3	4	hump
cat	deer	pig	lion	jellyfish	bison
5	6	7	8	9	10 ....

151

Reading 2

1 Read the text. Why do these animals have to adapt to their habitat?

ADAPTING to the Kalahari

Whistling rats live in the Kalahari Desert in southern Africa. The Kalahari is a very dry habitat. There's no rain in the winter for six to eight months. It's hot during the day, but temperatures can fall to -12 degrees Celsius at night. The ground is sandy, and there aren't many plants or trees.

Whistling rats have sandy-colored fur and this helps them hide in the desert. They have short, round ears, and they can hear very well. They give a loud whistle when a snake or a bird comes close. Then they run very quickly and jump into their holes underground. They're usually herbivores, and they eat plants not far from home, so they can escape easily when danger is close.

Kalahari lions also adapted to life in the desert. They have long, thin legs, and bigger paws than other lions. This helps them travel long distances to look for food and water. Kalahari lions can go up to two weeks without drinking water! They get some water from the animals they eat.

They live in smaller groups than other lions. This is because there aren't many big animals for them to hunt, so they eat animals like antelopes, birds, porcupines, and mice. These are also easier to catch, so the lions don't waste energy.

To cool down, they lie on their backs with their mouths open and their paws facing upward. This is because they sweat through their paws and mouths.

2 Complete the chart for how the Kalahari lion adapts to its habitat.

Body	Food	Behavior

3 Think and write.

1 Why is it important for animals to be adaptable?

....

2 How do humans adapt to the places they live?

....

Grammar 2

Describing words in a sentence go in a fixed order. The order depends on what each words is describing and it is: size, shape, color, place/origin.
a **big**, **round**, **purple**, **Antarctic** octopus

1 Read and categorize the underlined words.

C = color   N = name   O = origin   S = size   SH = shape

1 I have a [small] [round] [brown] bag.
       S   SH   C

2 There are many [big] [black and white] [Antarctic] [penguins].
       ....

3 We saw an [enormous] [brown] [African] lion at the zoo.
       ....

4 There's a [large] [round] [red] [clock] on my bedroom wall.
       ....

2 Look, read, and choose.

1 It's a(n) ...... bear.
   a brown, big, American
   b American, big, brown
   c big, brown, American

3 They're ...... krill.
   a yellow and brown, small
   b small, yellow and brown
   c yellow, small and brown

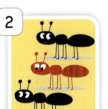

2 They're ...... ants.
   a red, tiny, black
   b tiny, red and black
   c red and black, tiny

4 It's a(n) ...... spider.
   a giant, black, Australian
   b Australian, giant, black
   c Australian, black, giant

153

3 Look and read. Then read and complete using one, two, or three words.

At the zoo

Last weekend, Joe and his family went to the zoo. They saw six monkeys from Africa. They were small, brown, and really funny! Next, they saw two green snakes. They were long and scary. Joe's little sister didn't like them. There were some dolphins, too. They were gray.

Joe's favorite animals at the zoo were the parrots from Australia. Their feathers were very colorful and they were very smart. After that, the family had a picnic. They sat on a big, red blanket. They ate cheese sandwiches. They were small and triangular. What a great day!

1 There were six _small, brown, African_ monkeys at the zoo. They were funny.

2 There were two .... snakes. They were scary.

3 There were some .... dolphins.

4 There were some .... parrots. They were smart.

5 They sat on a .... picnic blanket.

6 They ate .... cheese sandwiches.

4 Look and write two sentences for each picture. Use two or three describing words in each sentence.

1 It's a ....
2 ....

3 ....
4 ....

154

Writing

1 Read and underline words that make the writing stronger.

There are many amazing animals in the world that are in danger. The incredible Bornean orangutan is one of them. Orangutans aren't huge, but can weigh up to 100 kg. They have long, orange hair and strong arms that help them swing from tree to tree. They eat mostly fruit and leaves, but sometimes also termites and ants.

They live on the stunning isle of Borneo in tropical rainforests. When people cut down trees, they destroy this wonderful animal's habitat.

2 Read and make notes about your animal.

1 Where does it live?

....

2 What does it eat?

....

3 What does it look like?

....

4 Why is it in danger?

....

3 Write a report about your animal. Use your ideas from Activity 2 to help you.

(!) Remember
1 Write a title.
2 Use paragraphs.
3 Use extreme descriptions.

155

Now I Know

1 Read and circle.

1 A group of explorers traveling to study a place.   **expedition / crack**
2 Europe, America, Australia, and Asia are this.   **layer / continent**
3 We use them to describe how hot or cold it is.   **degrees / freezing**
4 A bird that lives in very cold places. It can't fly.   **penguin / feathers**
5 We say this when it's very cold.   **deep / freezing**
6 Water becomes this at zero degrees.   **ice / krill**
7 Birds have these on their skin.   **cracks / feathers**
8 This type of material keeps you dry.   **waterproof / poisonous**
9 Birds use these to fly.   **wings / fur**
10 Some animals do this to get food.   **layer / hunt**
11 This kind of food or drink can kill you.   **poisonous / freezing**
12 A small sea creature that whales eat.   **krill / feather**

2 Read and match.

1 There's   a any sugar in this tea?
2 There aren't   b any milk in the fridge.
3 Are there any   c people in the room?
4 There isn't   d a bag of tomatoes on the table.
5 Is there   e any books on the table.

3 Read and complete.

1 I'd like to visit the S_ _ _ _ _ _e and look for meteorites.
2 The ship sank _ee_ into the ocean after it hit an iceberg.
3 The _ _ _ _ _r_ _u_ _ is very high today. Let's go to the beach!
4 I have a brown _ _r coat, but it isn't real.
5 Zebras _ _g_ _ _e to find food and water.
6 A meteorite has many _a_ _ _s that can tell us amazing things about space.

156

4 Look and write the words in order.

1

elephant / gray / large / African
It's a ....

2

black / meteorites / round / small
They're ....

5 Check (✓) things you can count. Then choose three words and write sentences.

bottle ☐   chocolate ☐   ice ☐   milk ☐
octopus ☐   scientist ☐   water ☐   wing ☐

1 ....
2 ....
3 ....

Things I learn

1 What are your three favorite words in this unit?

....

2 Write something you think is interesting about:

expeditions ....

animals and their habitats ....

3 What are some of the ways animals and people adapt to extreme habitats?

....
....

157

12 Why do we have festivals?

1 What's the most important festival in your country? Write two things you like about festivals.

....

....

2 Circle the things people often do at festivals. Then think about and write one thing you learn in this unit.

    dance   eat traditional food   play tennis   read books
                      wear special clothes

....

3   Watch the video. Then look and write.

| celebration | float | pedometer | wooden frame |

1    2    3    4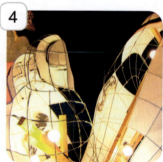

....

4 Read and match. Watch the video again to check.

1 A *nebuta* is a   a myths, legends, or history.
2 A *haneto* is a   b all year round at a museum.
3 The floats have themes from   c at the start of every August.
4 The festival takes place   d float made from a wooden frame and wire.
5 You can see the floats   e dancer.

Vocabulary 1

1 Find six words or phrases and label the pictures. There's one extra word.

fcocostumenstparadeinglanternoedemperorwstiltwalkerrgfireworks

1 .... 2 .... 3 .... 4 .... 5 ....

2 Read and circle.

Last week, I was in Patras – a big town in Greece. It was carnival! There was a big ¹ **parade / stilt walker** and people wore colorful ² **fireworks / costumes** and danced. The streets were very ³ **crowded / furry**. At night, we watched the ⁴ **parade / fireworks** in the sky. People lit ⁵ **lanterns / emperors** and let them fly. Our lantern didn't light up in the beginning and it was a bit ⁶ **furry / annoying**. But it finally worked and it looked so beautiful in the sky!

3 Write the letters in order. Then choose three words and write sentences.

1 y u f r r ....
2 n g a h ....
3 d d e c r o w ....
4 r o r p m e e ....
5 w f e o r i r k s ....
6 o y i n n n g a ....

....
....
....

4. Think about the last festival or a holiday you celebrated and write sentences. Use the words from the box.

costume   crowded   fireworks   lantern   parade

1 ......
2 ......
3 ......
4 ......
5 ......

Vocabulary challenge: things we have at festivals

5. Look and write. Use the words from the box.

bunting   confetti   marching band   streamers

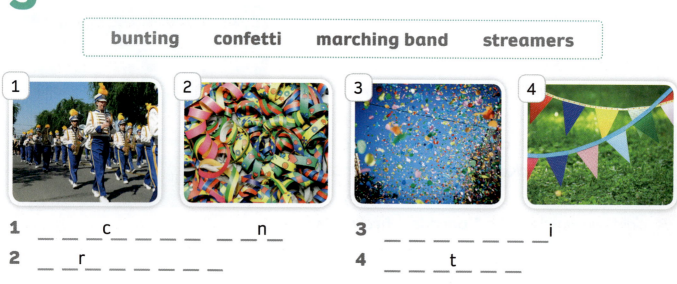

1 _ _ c _ _ _ _ _ _ _ n _
2 _ r _ _ _ _ _ _
3 _ _ _ _ _ _ _ i
4 _ _ t _ _ _

6. Read and complete. Use the words from Activity 5.

My Town Festival

Every year, there's a summer festival in my town. My sister plays the drums in a ¹.................... so we always watch her in the parade. There are a lot of floats in the parade, too. The people on the floats throw colorful ².................... and ³.................... in the air. After the parade, there's a party on our street. My friends and I put up the ⁴.................... and other decorations, and the adults make the food. It's really fun!

160

Reading 1

1 Read the story. Then write a short paragraph that retells it in your notebook. Use your own words.

THE SUITCASE

It was December 31st, and Ana and her family were almost ready to celebrate New Year.

"Go and put on your new dress," said Ana's mom. "It's eight thirty already!"

Ana ran up to her room to put on her best clothes. She was very excited. New Year was her favorite celebration. She loved the special meal that they ate only once a year, and the fireworks at midnight. This year she was even more excited because her uncle, aunt, and cousins were on their way. They lived in the south of Argentina, and Ana didn't see them often.

The buzzer rang, and Ana got to the door first. There stood her uncle and his family. "Hi, Ana! It's so good to see you again," said Aunt Cristina. "I have something important for later!" Ana looked down at the suitcase in her aunt's hand. She wondered what was inside.

After dinner, Ana's uncle let Ana open the suitcase. When Ana opened it, she was confused. "It's empty!"

"Follow me," said her uncle. He closed the suitcase, grabbed Ana's hand, and started running around the house.

"Why are we running?" asked Ana.

"It's a New Year's Eve tradition. It means next year will be full of adventure and travels," he explained. "Why don't you keep the suitcase? Write stories about your adventures and put them in the suitcase. Next year, we'll read about them together."

"This is the best gift ever!" Ana said.

2 Read the story again. Circle **T** (true) or **F** (false).

1 Ana was very excited because of her new dress.   T   F
2 Ana didn't see her cousins often.   T   F
3 The suitcase had some papers in it.   T   F

3 Ana thinks the empty suitcase is the best gift ever. Why?

161

Grammar 1

will and won't

You/He **will** find his family.   I/We **will not** be at school next week.
We'll see a lot of fireworks.   Alice/They **won't** finish early tonight.
There**'ll** be rice balls.

1 To make a positive prediction about the future, use *will*.
2 To make a negative prediction about the future, use *will not* or *won't*.
3 *Will* doesn't change depending on the person.

1 **Listen and draw lines.**
06

Dan   Harry   Alice   Thomas

Elena   Maria   Azra   Mario

2 **Write the words in order.**

1 'll / have / she / after school / dinner

....

2 won't / Tony / a costume / wear / at the festival

....

3 will / the new museum / visit / we / soon

....

3 Look and write sentences using *will* and *won't*.

1 make a soup / make a cake
She won't make a soup.
She'll _____ .

3 drive to school / walk to school

2 go swimming / play basketball

4 buy five candies / buy ten candies

4 Check (✓) the things you will do and cross (✗) the things you won't do this summer. Add two more activities. Then write sentences.

MY SUMMER VACATION PLAN ☀

go swimming ☐	wear sunglasses ☐	.... ✓
climb a mountain ☐	build sandcastles ☐	.... ✗
go camping ☐	eat ice cream every day ☐	

163

Vocabulary 2

1 Look and write. Use the words from the box.

> bell   cathedral   coconut   eel   get married
> grown-up   spray   sticky   water fight

1 ....
2 ....
3 ....
4 ....
5 ....
6 ....
7 ....
8 ....
9 ....

2 Read and write. Find the hidden word.

1 A word used to describe glue. ▢▢▢▢▢▢
2 It's when people don't have to go to work/school. ▢▢▢▢ ▢ ▢▢▢ ▢▢▢
3 A round, brown fruit that's white on the inside. ▢▢▢▢▢▢▢
4 This is when you have fun getting your friends wet. ▢▢▢▢▢ ▢▢▢▢▢
5 You ring this. ▢▢▢▢
6 Two people do this to become husband and wife. ▢▢▢ ▢▢▢▢▢▢▢
7 A person who is over 18 years old. ▢▢▢▢▢▢-▢▢
8 When you take a shower, you … yourself with water. ▢▢▢▢▢
9 A long, thin fish that looks like a snake. ▢▢▢

Hidden word: ....

164

3 Look and write sentences using words from Activities 1 and 2.

Trish and John's wedding, 1952

....
....
....
....

Word study: compound words

4 Read and match.

1 grown-   a games
2 water   b band
3 marching   c up
4 day   d off
5 video   e fight

5 Read and complete. Use the words from Activity 4.

1 Having a .... is a great way to cool down on a hot day.
2 It's raining, so I think I'll stay at home and play ....
3 The people in the .... wore smart uniforms.
4 When I'm a .... , I'll stay up late every night.
5 In the United States and the U.K., most people have a .... on December 25th.

165

Reading 2

1 Read the article. Then complete the chart for the two festivals in the article and another festival you know.

NATURE FESTIVALS

Hanami

We asked Noriko, from Japan, about a famous festival that will take place next month.

Noriko, what is Hanami?

It's an ancient festival that happens when the cherry blossoms (the flowers on cherry trees) open. It's usually in March or April. Hanami means *looking at flowers* in Japanese.

Where will you go to look at cherry blossoms?

I'll go to the park with my family. There are a lot of beautiful trees there. We'll sit under the cherry trees and have a picnic.

What will you eat at the picnic?

We always take lunchboxes full of delicious food. This year I'll also take wagashi, which are Japanese sweets, and cherry blossom biscuits, my favourites!

BLOEMENCORSO BOLLENSTREEK

We asked Bram, from the Netherlands, about a famous flower festival.

What is Bloemencorso Bollenstreek?

It's a parade with lots of flowers. It takes place every April. It's the biggest flower festival in the world.

What entertainment will be there?

There will be music and theatre performances. There'll also be food stalls, so you can try traditional Dutch food, like little round pancakes called poffertjes.

What will you do there?

I'll take part in the parade. It's almost 12 hours long, but it's a lot of fun. All the floats are made of flowers. Thousands of people come to watch the parade. You have to come early to get a good spot.

	Hanami	Bloemencorso Bollenstreek	
Reason for festival	cherry blossom		
Month			
Special events			
Food			

2 Why is it important to keep traditions alive?

....

Grammar 2

Questions about the future

a **Who will you** invite next week?   I'll invite my friends.
   What will she do this year?   She'll go to high school.
   Where will he go?   He'll go to the movies.
   When will they arrive?   They'll arrive tonight.
   How will you get there?   I'll get there by bus.

b **Will there be** fireworks at the Snow Festival?
   Yes, there will. / **No, there won't.**

Questions in group "a" need information in the answer.
Questions in group "b" need *yes* or *no* in the answer.

1 Read and circle. Then match.

1 **Where** / **What** will Ben go tomorrow?
2 **Who** / **Will** Penny buy a car in two years?
3 **Where** / **How** will you get to the library?
4 **Will** / **Who** will be with you at the party?
5 **What** / **When** will they study next year?

a Himari will be with me.
b They'll study French.
c He'll go to the library.
d I'll ride my bike.
e Yes, she will.

2 Read and complete the questions. Then look and write the answers.

What   Where

.... will Cody take his brother?

....

How   Will

.... he eat pasta for dinner?

....

167

3 Write the words in order. Then look and write the answers.

1 people / live / where / will / in 2083

....
.... ?
....
....

2 will / travel / people / how

....
.... ?
....
....

3 aliens / live / people / will / with

....
.... ?
....
....

4 wear / people / what / will

....
.... ?
....
....

4 Complete the questions. Then answer for you.

1 .... (where/you/live) in ten years?
    ....

2 .... (you/go) to a festival next year?
    ....

3 .... (what/job/you/do) when you finish school?
    ....

4 .... (who/you/visit) next weekend?
    ....

Writing

1 Read and circle the time phrases.

A Festival I Love: Holi

Next month, it'll be Holi. It's an ancient festival celebrated in India. It celebrates the beginning of spring and usually takes place in March.

Every year, we throw different-colored powder at each other. This year, I'll throw red and blue powder – my favorite colors. Next week, my friends and I will go downtown to buy powder for the festival.

In the evening, after playing with colors all day, we will clean up, dress up, and spend time with our friends and family. I can't wait!

2 Read and make notes about your favorite festival.

1   What does the festival celebrate?

3   Who will you go with?

2   When is it?

4   What will you do there?

3 Write about your favorite festival. Use your ideas from Activity 2 to help you.

(!) Remember
1   Write a title.
2   Use paragraphs.
3   Use time phrases.
4   Write neatly.

169

Now I Know

1 Look and complete the crossword.

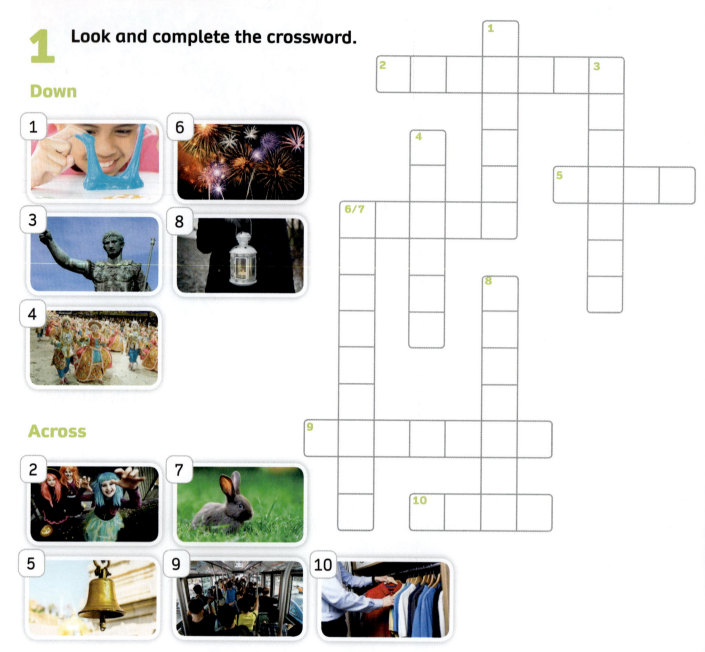

2 Read and complete. Use the words from the box.

> annoying   cathedral   eels   get married   water fight

1 Will you _____ and have a family when you're older?
2 There was a _____ at the end of the festival – I got very wet!
3 We didn't swim in the river because there were too many _____ in it.
4 The old _____ in the town square is very beautiful.
5 My baby sister can be _____ , but I love her anyway.

3 Look at May's predictions for her school vacation. Then read the answers and complete the questions.

May's vacation plans

Monday	Tuesday	Wednesday	Thursday	Friday
play baseball	visit Andrew	swimming pool	visit my cousins	ride my bike to the park

1 When ....?
   On Thursday.
2 What ....?
   Play baseball.
3 Will .... on Tuesday?
   Yes, she will.
4 How ....?
   By bike.

Things I learn

1 What are your three favorite words in this unit?

....

2 Write something you think is interesting about:

festivals around the world   ....
traditions in other countries   ....

3 How do festivals help bring people together?

....
....

171

Pearson Education Limited
KAO TWO
KAO Park
Hockham Way
Harlow, Essex
CM17 9SR
England
and Associated Companies throughout the world.

www.English.com

© Pearson Education Limited 2019

The right of Catherine Zgouras to be identified as author of this Work has been asserted by her in accordance with the Copyright, Designs and Patents Act 1988.

All rights reserved; no part of this publication may be reproduced, stored in a retrieval system, or transmitted in any form or by any means, electronic, mechanical, photocopying, recording, or otherwise without the prior written permission of the Publishers.

First published 2019

ISBN: 978-1-292-21955-4

Set in Daytona Pro Primary

Printed and bound by L.E.G.O. S.p.A. Italy

Image Credit(s):
123RF.com: 1xpert 145, Alexander Raths 160, Alexbrylov 117, Andrey Gudkov 155, Belchonock 143, 150, 61, BlueOrange Studio 150, Bogdan Mircea Hoda 122, Bombaert 5, Byrdyak 170, Delcreations 117, Destinacigdem 34, 76, Dinodia 131, Dmitriy Shironosov 170, Duncan Noakes 151, Elizaveta Galitckaia 137, Ewastudio 75, Famveldman 65, Fotocromo 75, Graham Oliver 65, Iakov Filimonov 95, Igor Bondarenko 79, Invictus99 75, Jakobradlgruber 5, James Kirkikis 150, Jan Skwara 80, Jane Rix 29, Josef Muellek 78, Konstantin32 104, Kzenon 95, Lightfieldstudios 95, Markus Gann 47, Martii Tapio Salmela 108, Mathier 76, Maxim Petrichuk 151, Maya23k 131, Mikkel Bigandt 111, Mspurny 20, Neelsky 150, Noppharat Prathumthip 34, Olegdudko 67, Pavel Losevsky 10, Prykhodov 67, Rapeepan Naksamruaj 61, Rigamondis 47, Sandra Dombrovsky 122, Scyther5 72, Sean Prior 122, Sergey Skleznev 20, Sergii Mostovyi 160, Shao-Chun Wang 137, Siam Pukkato 61, 75, Siraphol 79, Sonja Rachbauer 170, Sunanta Boonkamonsawat 122, Tan4ikk 109, Tatsiana Matusevich 78, Teeramet Thanomkiat 143, Tetiana Zbrodko 61, Tinna2727 131, Tombaky 34, Vadim Sadovski 109, Viacheslav Iakobchuk 137, Viperagp 78, Vladislav Zhukov 38, Volodymyr Golubyev 67, Volodymyr Krasyuk 76, Whitestar1955 66, Xtrekx 72, Yuliya Lapkovkaya 80, италий Мамчук 124; **Alamy Stock Photo:** Alex Segre 50, Blend Images 36, Cultura Creative (RF) 141, David Wall 38, Design Pics Inc 146, EnVogue_Photo 61, Ivan Nesterov 122, MITO images GmbH 89, NASA Photo 110, 147, OJO Images Ltd 50, Robertharding 170, Simon Dack 67, Tetra Images 104, 95, Thanostdm 159, Tim Gainey 169, View Stock 27; **BBC Worldwide Learning:** BBC - Co-Branded Products 102, 116, 130, 144, 158, 18, 32, 4, 46, 60, 74, 88; **Getty Images:** Alistair Berg 38, Andersen Ross 50, Blend Images-Jon Feingersh 95, FatCamera 138, Fstop123 55, Hedgehog94 170, Henn Photography 68, Hero Images , Jovanmandic 38, Jupiterimages 50, Kali9 85, Lido Frazao 26, Mario Eduardo Koufios Fraiz 44, Mike Powles 20, Nick Clements 96, Tomas Rodriguez 50, TongoRo Images Inc 104, Usas 137, Westend61 50; **Shutterstock.com:** 635926 150, Aaron Wood 170, Addkm 75, Africa Studio 131, 75, 79, 95, Alones 114, Andy Dean Photography 28, Anetlanda 131, Anna Nahabed 131, Anon Prasert 80, Art Neli 79, Bobkeenan Photography 117, Bullwinkle 117, Carlos E.Santa Maria 170, Chantal de Bruijine 150, Chanut Wongrattana 19, Christian Bertrand 99, Cyhe 108, Daniel Lohmer 65, Dean Drobot 104, 75, Dmitry Kalinovsky 28, 75, Dmytro Zinkevych 80, Fluke Samed 75, Foxy burrow 131, Gengirl 20, Gil.K 124, Hafizussalam bin Sulaiman 80, Harper 3D 20, HelloRF Zcool 72, Hin255 19, Hiroshi Teshigawara 66, JMx Images 152, Janis Smits 34, Jarabee123 170, Joe Belanger 72, John McQueen 5, Jukka Jantunen 151, Kateryna Omelianchenko 93, Kevin Eaves 72, Kravik93 47, Laborant 12, LeManna 131, Leavector 29, Life science 137, Lucky Business 66, Lurii 47, Maciej Es 47, Magic mine 72, MarcelClemens 109, Marian Weyo 136, MaxFX 5, Mazri Yaakub 65, Mechanik 109, Melinda Nagy 160, Monkey Business Images 10, NASA Images 108, Narcis Parfenti 10, Neirfy 89, Nejron Photo 89, OlegD 127, Orxy 72, Pabkov 117, Paulo Resende 34, Photobank.ch 10, Pierre-Yves Babelon 65, Piotr Krzeslak 65, Pressmaster 131, Pryzmat 66, Radovan1 117, Richard Thornton 160, Rjmiguel 5, S-F 10, Sean Pavone 10, Sergey Nivens 108, ShutterProductions 66, Simone Andrioletti 127, Songquan Deng 5, Stanisic Vladimir 75, Stockcreations 79, Taiftin 78, Testing 170, Tono Balaguer 137, Tracy Whiteside 104, Treter 26, Triff 109, Tund 79, Usanee 151, VGstockstudio 131, VaLiza 104, Vadim Sadovski 108, Valeri Potapova 151, Valerii Lavtushenko 170, Viktor1 78, Vitalina Rybakova 78, Vitaly Korovin 75, Vittorio Bruno 151, Vyacheslav Svetlichnyy 66, Wjarek 166, YapAhock 72, Zaitsava Olga 75.

Cover Images: *Front:* **Getty Images:** Hero Images

Illustrated by Keri Green (Beehive Illustration) p.6, 11, 16, 17, 19, 22, 23, 24, 32, 39, 42, 45, 54, 56, 58, 61, 62, 64, 67, 82, 83, 84, 86, 90, 94, 101, 103, 106, 112, 118, 119, 121, 128, 134, 139, 140, 149, 154, 159, 162, 164, 168; The Boy Fitz Hammond (NB Illustration) p. 8, 9, 14, 21, 28, 31, 33, 35, 40, 49, 52, 53, 63, 70, 78, 79, 87, 91, 92, 97, 98, 120, 125, 132, 133, 135, 148, 153, 157, 161, 163, 165, 167; Juanbjuan Oliver (Beehive Illustration) p. 105; Duscan Pavlic (Beehive Illustration) p. 77; Marina Pessarrodona (Astound US) p. 47